MOISTURE IN TEXTILES

OMNIA·SUNT
PENDENTIA·FILO
HOMINUM·TENUI

MOISTURE IN TEXTILES

Edited by

J. W. S. HEARLE, M.A., PH.D., A.INST.P.
Manchester College of Science and Technology

PROFESSOR R. H. PETERS, B.SC., PH.D.
Manchester College of Science and Technology

NEW YORK
TEXTILE BOOK PUBLISHERS, INC.
A Division of
INTERSCIENCE PUBLISHERS, INC.

MANCHESTER & LONDON
THE TEXTILE INSTITUTE
BUTTERWORTHS SCIENTIFIC PUBLICATIONS
1960

BUTTERWORTHS PUBLICATIONS LTD.
88 KINGSWAY, LONDON, W.C.2.

THE TEXTILE INSTITUTE
10 BLACKFRIARS ST., MANCHESTER 3

U.S.A. Edition published by
TEXTILE BOOK PUBLISHERS, INC.
A Division of
Interscience Publishers, Inc.
250 Fifth Avenue, New York, 1, N.Y.

Set in Monotype Baskerville type
Printed in Great Britain by Spottiswoode, Ballantyne and Co. Ltd.
London and Colchester

CONTENTS

LIST OF CONTRIBUTORS

J. Crank, M.Sc., D.Sc., F.Inst.P. (Courtaulds Ltd., Maidenhead)*

J. W. S. Hearle, M.A., Ph.D., A.Inst.P. (Manchester College of Science and Technology)

P. S. H. Henry, B.A., Ph.D. (British Cotton Industry Research Association)

G. King, M.Sc. (Wool Industries Research Association)

Professor R. Meredith, D.Sc., F.Inst.P., F.T.I., F.R.S.E. (British Cotton Industry Research Association)†

W. H. Rees, B.Sc., M.Sc., F.Inst.P. (British Cotton Industry Research Association)

A. R. Urquhart, D.Sc., F.R.I.C., F.T.I. (Lansil Ltd., Lancaster)‡

Present Addresses:

* Brunel College of Technology, Acton, London N.W.3.

† Royal College of Science and Technology, Glasgow.

‡ British Cotton Industry Research Association.

PREFACE

The interactions of moisture and fibres have many technical consequences: the weight changes are of direct financial importance, and they may also influence the composition of a blend or the apparent count of a yarn. Because of the associated heat effects, conditioning is a slow process, and textiles buffer changes of temperature which the body would otherwise experience. Swelling results in dimensional changes of yarns and fabrics—sometimes this is advantageous, as in the closing of pores of Ventile fabrics, but more often it is a nuisance, causing garments to become ill-fitting. The changes in mechanical properties, such as the increased strength of wet cotton and the lower strength of wet rayon, influence the behaviour of textiles under different atmospheric conditions. The amount of water absorbed by fibres varies considerably. In general, those which absorb most water are easier to dye, more prone to microbiological attack, less prone to static electrification and better conductors of electricity.

These topics, together with explanations of the phenomena in terms of physico-chemical concepts, form the subject of this book, which has been based on a series of lectures held at the Manchester College of Science and Technology. The course was organized by Dr. J. M. Preston on behalf of the Departments of Textile Chemistry and Textile Industries in the College and given under the auspices of the Manchester and District Advisory Council for Further Education.

R. H. PETERS
J. W. S. HEARLE

June, 1959

Chapter 1

WATER AND THE ATMOSPHERE

By P. S. H. Henry

This book is mainly concerned with the relationships between the content of moisture in a fibre and that in the atmosphere, and with the effects, such as heat changes, which occur during the sorption process. However, before discussing detailed relationships it is considered necessary to define what is meant by relative humidity and to describe some of the phenomena associated with changes in relative humidity which impinge on our everyday life.

DEFINITION OF RELATIVE HUMIDITY

The moisture content of textile materials depends not only on the properties of the textile, but also on external factors, the most important being the relative humidity and the temperature. The definition of the former is by no means fully standardized as befits a quantity of such importance to textiles, and several definitions have been used in the past. More than a matter of wording is involved, as may be exemplified by the three definitions of relative humidity which are tabulated below in abbreviated form with the physical quantities involved noted alongside.

Definition	Quantities Involved
1. Ratio of actual vapour pressure to that in equilibrium with liquid water.	Ratio of two pressures.
2. Ratio of mass of vapour in unit volume of the moist air to the mass contained at saturation.	Ratio of two densities (or concentrations).
3. Ratio of mass of vapour present in unit mass of dry air to the mass of vapour present in unit mass of air saturated with moisture.	Ratio of two ratios ('moisture contents').

The second definition differs from the first only in so far as water vapour disobeys the perfect gas laws because of molecular association or other effects. The maximum difference does not exceed 1 part in 1,000 at room temperatures, but may rise to 1 part in 60 near the boiling point (*1*).

The third definition differs from the second mainly in taking a given quantity of dry air as the basis for expressing composition, rather than a given quantity of the moist air. The difference is thus arithmetical rather than physical, and, whilst small at room temperatures, becomes large near the boiling point. At 100°C and an atmospheric pressure of 760 mm of mercury, a given mass of air is, at equilibrium, accompanied by a virtually infinite amount of water vapour; hence, any actual mixture of air and vapour under these conditions has a relative humidity of zero according to the third definition. This is an obvious disadvantage of the definition, since the notion of relative humidity is still useful at temperatures up to, and indeed above, the boiling point.

There is little to choose between the first and second definitions, but the first does not refer to the air, and is equally useful whether this is present or not. British Standard 1339:1946, entitled 'Humidity of the Air (Definitions, Formulæ, and Constants)' uses the first definition, with the words 'The ratio of the actual vapour pressure to the saturation vapour pressure at the same (dry bulb) temperature, expressed as a percentage'. It may be remarked that B.S. 1051:1953 'Moisture in Textile Materials' uses a method of defining relative humidity which is equivalent to the second definition, and is thus inconsistent with B.S. 1339. The difference is numerically negligible at higher temperatures.

The quantity specified in the third definition is given the name 'Percentage Saturation' in B.S. 1339.

EFFECT OF AIR UPON RELATIVE HUMIDITY

It is common to speak of 'the relative humidity of the air', but it is not necessary to mention air in the definition, nor is it relevant, to a first approximation, to the notion of relative humidity. The presence or absence of air would be important if it affected either the actual water vapour pressure or its saturation value. It does, in fact, affect both, but only slightly. We can get an idea of the order of magnitude of the effect by considering the alteration in the saturation vapour pressure produced by the presence of air at atmospheric pressure. There are three causes to consider:

(*a*) the total pressure on the liquid,

(*b*) solution of air in the liquid, and

(*c*) the intermolecular forces between water and air molecules in the gas phase.

The first two effects are readily calculable by thermodynamic principles from simple observed quantities. For a liquid–vapour system, it can be shown (*2*) that an increase ΔP in total pressure P produces an increase $\delta p = \Delta P . V/v$ in equilibrium vapour pressure p_s, where V and v are the volumes of a given amount of water as liquid and vapour, respectively at pressures P and p_s. If V and v refer to 1 mole of water, and if we may apply the equation for a perfect gas, the proportional increase in saturated vapour pressure is given by

$$\delta p/p = \Delta PV/RT$$

When ΔP is equal to normal atmospheric pressure, this equation shows that the increase in the equilibrium vapour pressure of water at room temperature is rather less than 1 part in 1,000. The pressure of vapour in equilibrium with a moist textile will be affected in a similar way, so that the relative humidity in equilibrium with the textile will change by less than 1 part in 1,000.

The effect of air dissolved in the liquid water can also be calculated from the experimental values for the solubilities of the chief components of air in equilibrium with their respective partial pressures. At 20°C a litre of water in equilibrium with air contains 12·3 ml of nitrogen, 6·4 ml of oxygen, and not more than 2·6 ml of carbon dioxide. The total concentration of the components is 0·89 millimoles per litre, or a mole fraction of $1{\cdot}6 \times 10^{-5}$. It follows from Raoult's law (*3*) that the proportional lowering of the vapour pressure is equal to the same fraction, and is quite negligible.

The effect of intermolecular forces in the gas phase is less easy to calculate, and no data seem to be available from which it can be done. This effect is almost always ignored in calculations dealing with small amounts of water vapour in air, and is not likely to cause trouble. The fact that air molecules are less polar than water molecules suggests that, at higher temperatures and humidities, when the number of water molecules per unit volume is comparable with that of air molecules, the effect of their interactions will be less than that between the water molecules themselves. As previously mentioned, this is small, though not quite negligible.

We can therefore conclude that the presence of air has an insignificant effect on the vapour pressure of water in textile systems and is irrelevant to the definition of relative humidity in this connection.

OTHER WAYS OF EXPRESSING HUMIDITY

Definitions of absolute humidity, moisture content (of air), saturation deficit, and other quantities can be found in B.S. 1339, together with useful data showing the relations between them. There would be no point in repeating these here. In work on textiles, relative humidity is the most useful quantity, since the equilibrium moisture regain for a given *relative* humidity varies only slightly with the temperature; hence, provided that the relative humidity is known, it is not very important to know the temperature. If the absolute humidity were used it would be just as important to know the temperature as to know the humidity. This difference is illustrated in *Figure 1*, where the left-hand graph shows the well-known experimental results of Urquhart and Williams (*4*) for the equi-

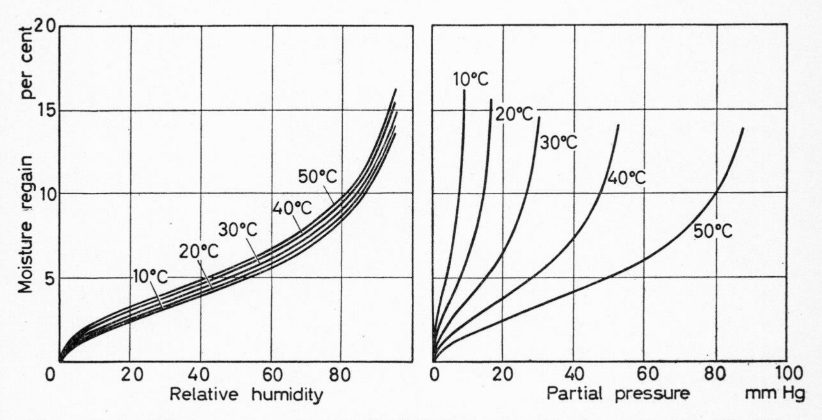

Figure 1. Equilibrium moisture regain of soda-boiled cotton plotted against relative humidity (left-hand graph) and against partial pressure of water vapour (right-hand graph)

librium moisture regain (absorbing) of soda-boiled cotton plotted against humidity for a range of temperatures from 10°C to 50°C. The right-hand graph shows the same results replotted against the partial pressure of the water vapour; the curves for the different temperatures are now widely separated.

Another way of stating the same facts, which is perhaps more enlightening from the physicist's point of view, is to say that a textile containing a given amount of moisture has an equilibrium vapour pressure which remains a roughly constant fraction of that of pure water as the temperature varies.

Though the relative humidity is the most convenient form in which to express the amount of moisture in the air under equilibrium conditions, it may be better to use the absolute humidity or one of the other related quantities when the problem concerns rates of change, for instance, the drying of textiles in a forced draught.

VARIATION OF RELATIVE HUMIDITY WITH SEASON AND TIME OF DAY

The upper (continuous) curves in *Figure 2* show the variation in the mean (hourly) relative humidity outdoors at Kew for four different months in the year (*5*). There is a strong diurnal variation, especially during the summer, the relative humidity being highest at night and reaching a minimum during the early afternoon. The daytime relative humidity is highest during the winter, but at night the mean relative humidity is almost the same throughout the year. Examination of other data shows that the absolute humidity outdoors shows little, if any, diurnal variation, and that the large difference in

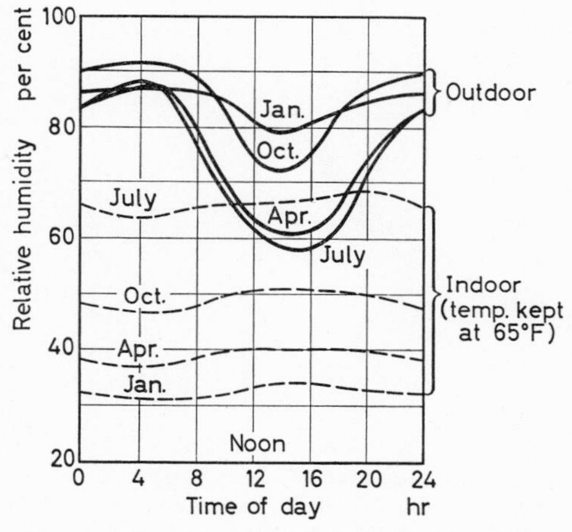

Figure 2. Diurnal variation of relative humidity at Kew

relative humidity between day and night is solely due to changes in temperature. The approximately constant mean relative humidity at night throughout the year is due to the higher absolute humidity during the summer nearly compensating for the higher temperature.

A better idea of the variation throughout the year of the mean day and night relative humidities is given in *Figure 3* for three locations in the British Isles (*5*). It should be realized that the shaded areas here do not represent the total ranges of relative humidity for different sorts of weather, but only the regular diurnal variation of the average. Any variation due to weather changes is superposed on this. Valentia is an island off the extreme south-west point of Eire, and the weather there is that of an Atlantic coastal station. The weather at Kew is representative of that for an inland situation with its much greater variation of temperature.

It is much less easy to give figures for the average relative humidity indoors. The absolute humidity in a well-ventilated room may be not far from that outdoors, but the temperature may be higher or lower according to the time of year and day. It is clear that the temperature will vary much less than that outdoors, and accordingly a set of values for the mean relative humidity has been derived on the assumption that the temperature is always 65°F. The values are shown by the dotted curves in *Figure 2*. Since the temperature is

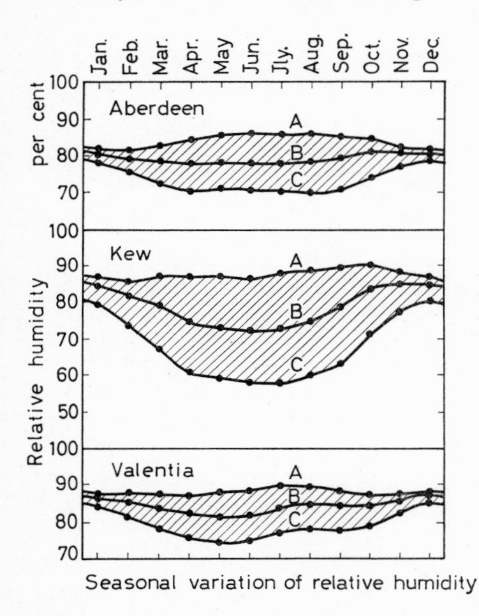

Figure 3. Seasonal variation of relative humidity: A—Early morning (max. of hourly means); B—Mean for whole day; C—Afternoon (min. of hourly means)

assumed to be constant, they are virtually curves showing the variation in absolute humidity. It will be seen that there is little difference between day and night, and that the relative humidity is highest during the summer instead of during the winter.

EFFECT ON INDOOR HUMIDITY OF HUMAN BEINGS, BUNSEN BURNERS, ETC.

Both the human body and a gas burner release heat and moisture into the air; the heat will tend to reduce the relative humidity in a room, but the moisture to increase it. An electric radiator produces heat only, and therefore will cause the relative humidity to decrease. In practice, the walls and objects in a room exert a strong stabilizing effect on both temperature and humidity, but it is useful to calculate what would happen if all the heat and moisture given out by a man or burner remained in the air of a room. The failure of the results to correspond with observed facts is a good illustration of the stabilizing effect.

Table 1 gives the sensible heat loss (i.e., not including that required to evaporate the moisture) and the moisture loss from the skin and lungs of an average man doing light work in average indoor conditions (*6*). Comparable figures are also given for a Bunsen burner consuming gas with a calorific value of 450 B.t.u./ft³ at the rate of 20 ft³/hr, and for a 1-kilowatt electric radiator.

TABLE 1

	Sensible heat production		Moisture production
	kcals/hr	watts	g/hr
Average man	85	100	40
Bunsen burner	2,300	2,700	380
1 kW radiator	860	1,000	Nil

In a room of dimensions 10 ft × 15 ft × 10 ft at 20°C and 65% r.h., calculations show that the mass of air in the room is 48 kg, the thermal capacity of the air is 12 kcal/°C and the mass of moisture in the air is 480 g. If we make the (rather academic) assumption that all the moisture and heat evolved by one man in an hour remains in the air of this room, we find that moisture alone would raise r.h. by 5·5% to 70·5%. But the heat raises the temperature by 7·1°C to 27·1°C, thereby reducing the r.h. from 70·5% to 47·5%. Thus, the overall effect would be a *fall* in relative humidity. Experiment, however, shows that the relative humidity rises when several people are confined in an unventilated room for some time. This shows the falseness of the assumption that all the heat remains in the air. In fact, it has been shown (*7*) that, for a man sitting still under average room conditions, about 80% of his sensible heat loss may go direct to the solid surroundings by radiation, only 20% going to warm the air. Some experiments by Rees and Henry (*8*) showed that a similar state of affairs may hold inside a sun helmet, most of the heat being transferred by radiation.

STABILIZATION OF RELATIVE HUMIDITY BY WALLS, FURNITURE, ETC.

The capacity of a room to absorb moisture, i.e., the amount of moisture which has to be introduced to produce a given increase in relative humidity, is greatly increased by the solid objects in the room, especially if they are of a porous nature and absorbent, like cellulosic and wool textiles. Such articles help to stabilize the relative humidity against temporary disturbances arising from the opening of doors and so forth. As an example, the author works in a fair-sized room with an air-space having a moisture capacity of about 7 g of water per 1% r.h. On the desk in front of him there is a modest row of books whose capacity is probably of the order of 20 g of water per 1% r.h., or about three times that of the air space. It is true that the books would react rather slowly, because of their small exposed surface; they are quoted because their capacity is easy to estimate. Thus, to maintain any enclosure at a constant relative humidity, it is advisable to have a large weight of absorbing material present. This may not be convenient in a whole room, but is perfectly feasible in a conditioning box, which may, for example, be lined with several thicknesses of a cotton, viscose rayon or wool fabric. These materials will help to restore the value of the relative humidity quickly after the box has been opened for the insertion or withdrawal of samples. Conversely, an enclosure which is intended to be run at a variety of relative humidities should have the minimum of moisture-absorbing materials used in its construction, or it will be slow in reaching a new value of humidity.

DISTURBING EFFECT OF WINDOWS ON RELATIVE HUMIDITY

The relative humidity in a room is most easily maintained constant if the temperature is kept constant. The chief sources of disturbance, other than open doors, are the windows, even if they are kept closed. This is because their thermal insulation is much lower than that of a wall, as shown by the following figures (*9*), which give the rate of passage of thermal energy through unit area of walls and windows when the temperature difference between their two sides is 1°F.

	watts/ft²
9-in. solid brick wall, plastered inside	0·100
18-in. solid brick wall, plastered inside	0·062
9-in. cavity brick wall, plastered inside	0·085
Window, single panes	0·30
Window, double panes (old style)	0·18
Window, double pane, ¼-in. gap	0·17

The figures show that an ordinary window lets through three and a half times as much heat per unit area as a 9-in. cavity wall, or five times as much as an 18-in. solid wall. To take an example, from a room of which one side, measuring 15 ft × 10 ft, is an outside wall consisting of 9-in. cavity brickwork, and containing two windows each 3 ft 6 in. × 7 ft 0 in., 63% of the total heat is lost through the windows. (It is assumed that the other walls, the floor, and the ceiling face on to rooms at the same temperature, so that no heat is lost through them.) To put it another way, the total heat loss from the room would be halved if the windows were bricked up. Substituting double panes for the single glass in the windows would reduce the total heat loss by 27%.

REFERENCES

1 See, e.g., N. E. Dorsey, *Properties of Ordinary Water Substance*, Reinhold, New York, 1940, p. 56.
2 See, e.g., S. Glasstone, *Textbook of Physical Chemistry*, 2nd edn, Macmillan, London, 1956, p. 445.
3 See, e.g., S. Glasstone, *Textbook of Physical Chemistry*, 2nd edn, Macmillan, London, 1956, p. 625.
4 A. R. Urquhart and A. M. Williams, *J. Text. Inst.*, **15,** T559 (1924).
5 Fig. 3 and the data for Fig. 2 are used by permission of the author, E. G. Bilham, of *The Climate of the British Isles*, Macmillan, London, 1938.
6 See, e.g., C. L. Evans, ed., *Starling's Principles of Human Physiology*, 6th edn, Churchill, London, 1953, pp. 536, 1016.
7 E. F. DuBois, *Medical Sciences, University Series*, Stanford University Publications, 1937, Vol. 3, No. 4, Chap. 2.
8 W. H. Rees and P. S. H. Henry, *Brit. J. Ind. Med.*, **3,** 225 (1946).
9 E. Molloy and others, *Electrical Engineer, Reference Book*, Newnes, London, 1945, pp. 15–22, except last figure, which is from data supplied by Pilkington Bros, Ltd.

Chapter 2

THE STRUCTURE OF FIBRES

By J. W. S. Hearle

The moisture which is absorbed by fibres fits closely into their structure: the molecules of water and fibre are intimately mixed. It is therefore appropriate to include at the beginning of this book a brief account of the structure of fibres.

The molecules of almost all fibres consist of many similar units joined together in long chains. Thus, in native cellulose fibres there may be 2,000 to 3,000 units in the chain, in regenerated cellulose and cellulose acetate about 500 units, and in synthetic fibres at least 100 units. The basic repeat units in some of the most important types of fibre are shown in Table 2.

All the natural and regenerated animal and vegetable fibres contain within their molecules groups which strongly attract water. In cellulose, there are hydroxyl groups to which water molecules can be attached by hydrogen bonds. In the proteins, there are carbonyl (—C=O) groups in the main-chain, and other active groups in the side-chains.

In cellulose acetate fibres, which are derived from cellulose by the replacement of most of the hydroxyl groups by acetyl groups, the side-groups are inert and do not attract water strongly. Consequently, the moisture absorption of acetate is less than that of unmodified cellulose. When cellulose acetate was first made, it proved impossible to find a suitable solvent to spin the fully acetylated triacetate. The material was therefore hydrolysed to secondary acetate, in which, for every six hydroxyl groups in the original cellulose, there are five acetyl groups and one hydroxyl group. This is the most commonly produced form of acetate, but means of spinning triacetate have now been achieved, and triacetate fibres are now available.

Most of the fibres prepared from synthetic polymers show a still smaller attraction for water. In nylon there are some —C=O groups, but in Terylene and most of the vinyl and acrylic fibres there are no hydrophilic groups.

However, it is not only the molecular composition of fibres that influences moisture absorption: the geometric arrangement of the molecules also plays a part. There is a great deal of evidence to show

TABLE 2

BASIC CHEMICAL FORMULAE OF FIBRES

Fibre type	Examples: Natural	Examples: Man-made	Repeat unit in formula
Cellulose	Cotton Flax Jute	Viscose rayon Cuprammonium rayon	CH_2OH OH OH O O—CH CH—CH CH CH CH CH CH—CH O O—CH OH OH CH_2OH
Cellulose ester	Acetylated cotton	Triacetate Secondary acetate	$CH_3 \cdot COO \cdot CH_2$ $CH_3 \cdot COO$ $OOC \cdot CH_3$ O O—CH CH—CH CH CH CH CH CH—CH O O—CH $CH_3 \cdot COO$ $OOC \cdot CH_3$ $CH_2OOC \cdot CH_3$ (In secondary acetate, one-sixth of the $CH_3.COO$ groups are replaced by OH groups)
Protein	Wool Silk	Fibrolane Vicara	—N(H)—CH(R)—C(=O)— (There are 20 different side-groups, R, which may be included in the molecule)
Polyamide		Nylon 6.6 Nylon 6.10 Nylon 6 Nylon 11	—NH—$(CH_2)_n$—NH—CO—$(CH_2)_m$—CO— In nylon 6.6, $n = 6$, $m+2 = 6$; in nylon 6.10, $n = 6$, $m+2 = 10$; etc. —NH—$(CH_2)_r$—CO— In nylon 6, $r+1 = 6$; In nylon 11, $r+1 = 11$; etc.
Polyester		Terylene Dacron	—O—CH_2—CH_2—O—CO—⬡—CO—
Acrylic		Orlon Acrilan Courtelle	—CH_2—CH(CN)— (Commercial fibres are usually co-polymers, including other units of form —CH_2.CHR—; or mixtures of polymers)
Vinyl		Rhovyl Vinyon Dynel	—CH_2—CH(R)— (Various groups, R, and mixtures of them are possible)

that only part of a fibre is freely accessible to water molecules. The interiors of regions in which the molecules have crystallized are usually inaccessible.

Partial crystallization is an almost essential feature of fibre formation. In order to make good fibres, a material must have long-chain molecules, which are oriented more or less parallel to one another. It is the close linkage together of the molecules in the crystalline arrangement that maintains this oriented arrangement, and prevents a transformation to the disorder characteristic of an unstretched rubber. The features that encourage crystallization are strongly attractive forces between neighbouring molecules (for example, hydrogen bonding between neighbouring cellulose molecules) and compact regular molecules which will pack closely together. In many cases the detailed crystal structure has been worked out. Native cellulose has a crystal structure, known as cellulose I, which does not change when water is absorbed. On the other hand, the slightly different crystal structure of regenerated cellulose, known as cellulose II, does alter when water is absorbed, and this suggests that a small percentage of water can be fitted into a modified crystal lattice. Cellulose II is also found, either wholly or partly, in native cellulose fibres which have been modified by mercerization or some other chemical treatments.

In wool the situation is complicated because the molecule is usually held in a folded form by internal cross-links. On stretching, the molecules unfold and the crystal structure is transformed from that of α-keratin to that of β-keratin.

X-ray diffraction studies of fibres indicate that the small crystalline regions present in fibres are shorter in length than the molecules. This has led to the development of the fringed micelle theory, which suggests that a single long-chain molecule will pass through several crystalline regions, as illustrated in *Figure 4*. At the edges of the crystalline regions the molecules spread out and pass through disordered non-crystalline regions. A molecular structure of this sort is believed to occur in most fibres, although electron-microscopic observation of fine fibrils little thicker than the crystalline regions has cast some doubt on the details of the theory.

The non-crystalline regions are most important in moisture absorption. The molecules here are linked together only at the few points where they cross close to one another. Consequently, most of the active groups are available to the water molecules. The structure is comparatively open in that it is freely accessible to water, and, being a loose network, it is easily deformed (or swollen) to allow additional water molecules to enter.

The proportions of crystalline and non-crystalline material in a fibre can be estimated by various methods, none of which give results that are beyond doubt: some typical values are given in

Figure 4. Structure of an oriented partly crystalline fibre

Table 3. It will be noticed that regenerated cellulose shows a much higher accessibility than native cellulose: this is paralleled by its moisture absorption.

TABLE 3

FIBRE ACCESSIBILITY

Fibre	Percentage accessible to water
Cotton	40%
Mercerized cotton	50%
Nylon	50%
Viscose rayon	67%
Wool	80%

These two features of molecular composition and arrangement—the number of hydrophilic groups and their accessibility—are the important factors determining the general pattern of moisture absorption in fibres.

Chapter 3

SORPTION ISOTHERMS

By A. R. Urquhart

The first chapter of this book discusses the properties of moisture-laden air, and the second deals with the structure of fibres. The remainder of the book is concerned with the phenomena that occur when fibres are exposed to moisture; it is well known that in these circumstances fibres take up water, and that in consequence of this their properties are modified in various far-reaching ways. But before such effects can be properly studied it is essential to have available exact quantitative information about the way in which the amount of water taken up depends on the variables that control it, and it is with this topic that this chapter deals. Although the actual amount of water found in the fibre under any given set of conditions varies quite largely from one kind of fibre to another, the general relationships are fairly similar for all, and it will not greatly detract from generality if attention is devoted here mainly to cellulosic fibres, which from this point of view have been studied more than any other group. The application of the general principles to any other fibre for which data are available should not present undue difficulty.

A fibrous material exposed to unchanging external conditions attains ultimately a moisture content that remains constant so long as these conditions remain unaltered. This constancy of moisture content is not a static state but is the result of a dynamic equilibrium, in which the amount of water evaporating from the fibres in unit time is exactly counterbalanced by that condensing on them. The rate of evaporation depends on the amount of water already taken up and on the temperature, while the rate of condensation depends on the number of potential absorbing points on the fibre that are still unoccupied and on the concentration of water vapour in the surrounding atmosphere. Hence, the fundamental variables controlling the amount of water in the material are the constitution and structure of the fibre itself, the temperature and the concentration of water in the fibre surroundings; the *sorption isotherm* is the curve that expresses the relation, at any constant temperature, between the amount of water in the fibre and its concentration outside. The amount of water in the fibre is generally expressed as a fraction or percentage of the weight of dry fibre, when it is called 'moisture regain', though occasionally it is referred to the combined weight of fibre and water, when it is called 'moisture content'; the concentration of water in the surrounding atmosphere is expressed as the relative vapour pressure (the partial pressure of water vapour divided by the saturation vapour pressure at the temperature concerned), or by 100 times that value, commonly known as '% relative humidity'.

There are two groups of direct methods of determining sorption isotherms. In the first, the sample is maintained at given water-vapour pressures in an enclosed space and the changes in its mass are measured. A simple method of doing this with samples in weighing bottles has been described by Bull (*1*), water vapour at known pressures being provided by mixtures of sulphuric acid and water in varying proportions. Other modifications of this method have been used by Mellon *et al.* (*2*) and by Urquhart and Williams (*3*). If the apparatus is evacuated, the approach to equilibrium is speeded up (*4*). Continuous observation of the changes in weight of the sample may be made by hanging it on a quartz or tungsten spiral spring, as described by McBain (*5, 6*) and by others (*7, 8*). Ashpole (*9*) has described a way of making these experiments at high humidities, where there is a risk of supersaturation if the temperature is not very closely controlled, and the approach to equilibrium is slow.

The basic apparatus for the second group of methods consists of a bulb containing the fibre which is connected to a mercury manometer, or some other device for measuring vapour pressure, and through a tap to a reservoir of water. After the fibres and the space around them are dried, a known mass of water is admitted, and the vapour pressure is measured after equilibrium has been reached. Thus, the total mass of water present within and around the fibres is kept constant during a test. This is repeated for successive additions of water. This method yields more accurate results, especially in the difficult conditions at very low and very high humidities, though it has been criticized on the ground that the vapour pressure is changing during the approach to equilibrium (*10*). Details of the method have been described by Urquhart and Williams (*11*), and more recently Taylor (*12, 13*) has described a more elaborate arrangement specially for use below 4% r.h.

Sorption isotherms have been determined for many different systems, and five types of isotherm have been noted; these are shown diagrammatically in *Figure 5*. The uptake of moisture by fibres usually occurs according to the isotherm shown as Type II, with an occasional tendency towards Type III. It is not necessary to discuss in detail here the theoretical significance of the different types, but some indication of their origin is desirable, if only to provide a theoretical framework in which to fit the facts to be presented. It is generally agreed that the Type I isotherm is characteristic of sorption

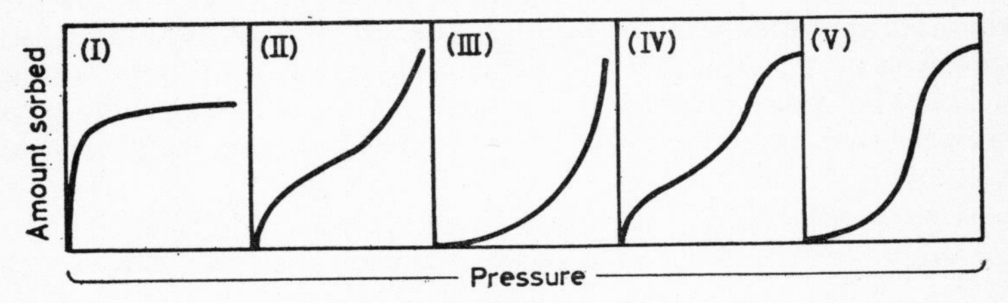

Figure 5. Types of sorption isotherm

where the substance forms only a unimolecular layer on the substrate, but there is more difference of opinion with regard to the remaining types. According to an all-embracing theory (*14*), the Type II iso-

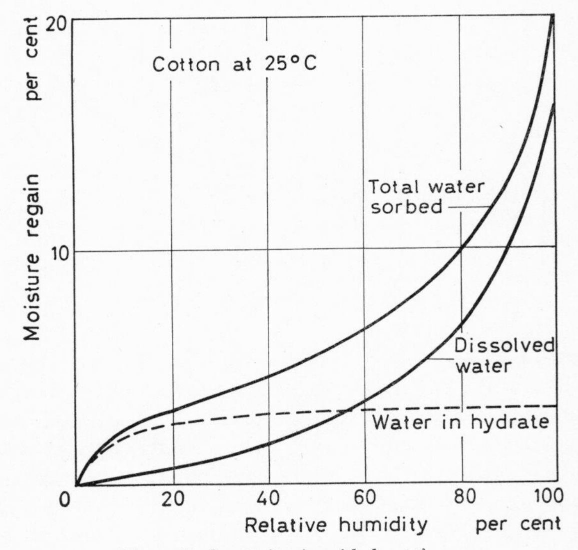

Figure 6. Composite sigmoid absorption curves

therm is characteristic of multimolecular sorption where the attractive forces between the sorbing and the sorbed substances are greater than those between the molecules of the sorbed substance in the liquid state, whereas Type III is obtained when the forces between sorbing and sorbed substances are relatively small. Types IV and V are obtained when the simpler relationships are complicated by the occurrence of capillary condensation. According to other, more circumscribed views (*15, 16*) an isotherm of Type II (the type in which we are principally interested) is the result of two simultaneously occurring processes, direct chemical combination of water molecules to fibre molecules producing one curve, while a looser binding by van der Waals forces or in solution provides the other; the sum of the

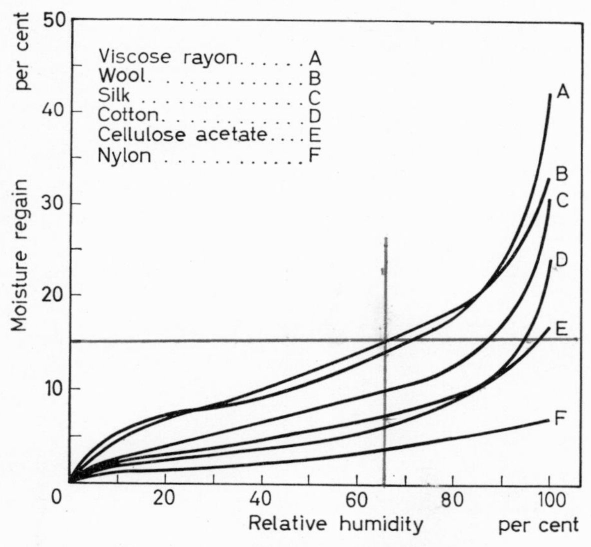

Figure 7. Sorption isotherms for textile fibres

two effects provides the composite sigmoid curve, as shown in *Figure 6*. That the isotherms of most textile fibres are of Type II will be clear from *Figure 7*, where isotherms for cotton, wool, silk, viscose rayon, cellulose acetate and nylon are shown.

So far sorption at one constant temperature only has been considered, and it is now necessary to examine what happens at other temperatures. All fibres in taking up moisture release heat, and it follows as a thermodynamic necessity that the amount of water taken up at constant relative humidity must decrease with increasing temperature. This effect has been studied in greatest detail for cotton (*17*), and *Figure 8*, which shows a series of isotherms for the sorption of water by scoured cotton at temperatures in the range 10–50°C, provides experimental confirmation of the theoretical deduction. In the range 50–110°C (*Figure 9*) the same effect is evident at relative humidities up to about 85%, but at higher humidities the curves cross one another, indicating that in this region the amount of water sorbed at constant humidity *increases* with increasing temperature. A similar effect has been found for wool (*18*). A possible explanation of this will be suggested later, but the picture is more complicated than would appear.

Figure 7 shows the isotherms for several fibres, each of which is

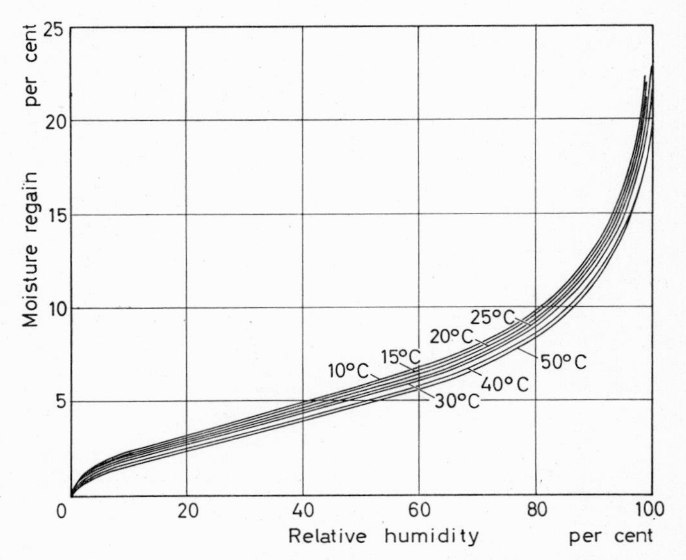

Figure 8. Effect of temperature (10–50°C) on sorption isotherms for cotton

represented by a single curve; this suggests that the moisture regain of a given fibre is uniquely determined by the temperature and the relative humidity. Any attempt to determine such a curve on this basis, however, would show that this supposition was incorrect, for difficulty would be experienced in obtaining reproducible results. The reason for this is that the amount of water depends not only on the temperature and humidity of the atmosphere to which the fibre is exposed, but also on the amount of water the fibre contained before exposure to that atmosphere. *Figure 10* shows the complete isotherm for scoured and dried cotton at 25°C (*11*). If dry cotton is placed in an atmosphere of given humidity, its moisture regain after equilibrium has been attained will correspond to the appropriate point on the lower of the two curves. If cotton that has been for some time in a saturated atmosphere is similarly exposed, its equilibrium moisture

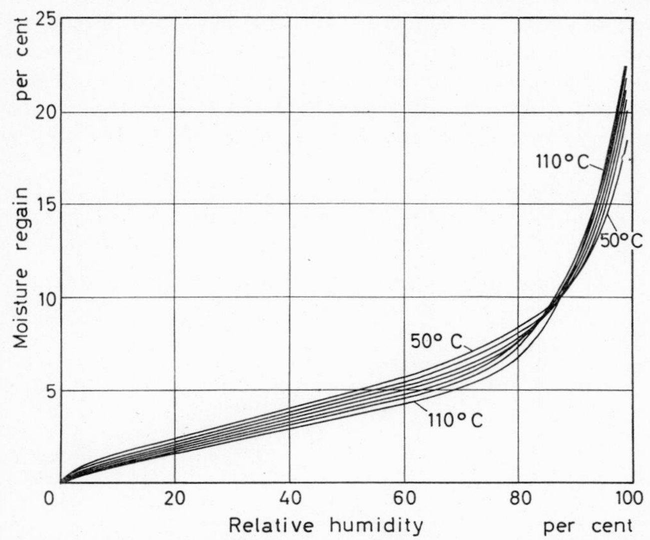

Figure 9. Effect of temperature (50–110°C) on sorption isotherms for cotton

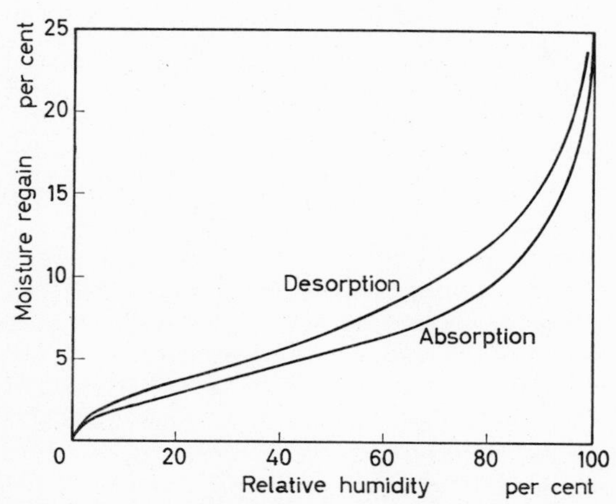

Figure 10. Sorption isotherm for scoured and dried cotton at 25°C

regain will be represented by a point on the upper curve. The divergence between the two values of the regain is usually quite large, as is the difference between the two humidities required to confer the same regain under these different conditions.

At first it was thought that this phenomenon, to which the name *hysteresis* has been given, was due to a very slow attainment of equilibrium, and that 'absorption' and 'desorption' * values would be identical if sufficient time were allowed for the 'true' equilibrium to be reached. There is ample evidence now, however, that the different values do, in fact, represent true equilibria. For example, samples

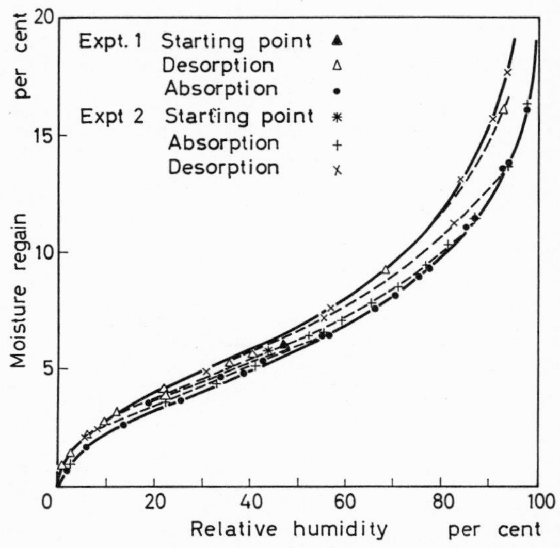

Figure 11. Effect of prehistory on sorption isotherm for raw cotton

brought from opposite directions into an atmosphere of medium humidity reached their different absorption and desorption equilibrium values in a few weeks; they were then allowed to remain in that atmosphere for over three years, and at the end of that time their regains were as far apart as they were at the beginning (*19*).

So far only the extreme variations that result from starting in a completely dry atmosphere on the one hand and a saturated atmosphere on the other have been considered. Experiment has shown that, where the differences of prehistory are less extreme, points between the absorption and desorption curves are obtained (*20*). This

* The word 'absorption' is used to denote 'sorption' when the amount of moisture in the material increases, and 'desorption' when it decreases, to the equilibrium value.

is illustrated by the curves of *Figures 11 and 12*, one for raw and the other for scoured cotton. From these figures it is apparent that any point between the two extreme curves may, under appropriate conditions of humidity and prehistory, represent the regain of a sample of the cotton in question, and hence that the specification of humidity and temperature does not uniquely define the amount of water in the fibre, but only the limits between which that amount shall lie. In other words, the two curves do not form an equilibrium locus but define an equilibrium area, and it is therefore important that these curves should themselves be specified with some accuracy.

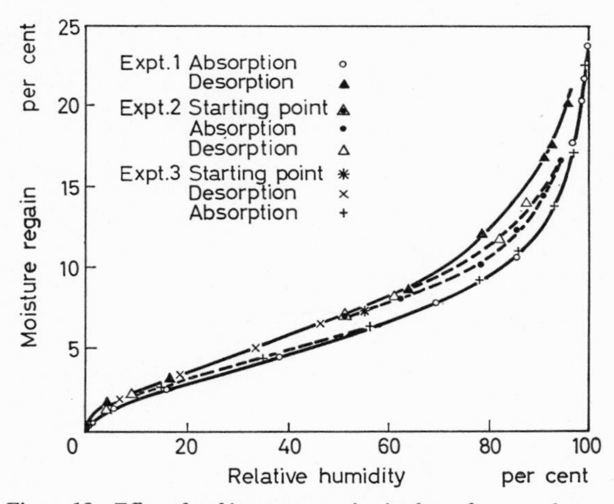

Figure 12. Effect of prehistory on sorption isotherm for scoured cotton

There is little difficulty about the lower limit; the absorption curve from dryness is obviously the locus of minimum moisture regains for any given material. The exact definition of the upper limit is less easy, for there is no apparent tendency for the hysteresis loop to close at the absorption saturation value. *Figure 13* shows that, if water is added to cotton after the saturation value has been reached, the desorption curve at humidities above 80% is higher the greater the original excess above the saturation value, so that the upper limit of the equilibrium area is obtained by removing water from thoroughly wet cotton. The explanation of this effect is probably that, if water in excess of the saturation value is added to the fibres in bulk, the spaces between the fibres will become filled, and their subsequent emptying will cause the water columns in these spaces to acquire curved surfaces, so that there will be a reduction of vapour pressure below the saturation pressure when the total amount of water present is still in excess of the absorption saturation value. It would follow, therefore, that this variability of the hygroscopicity at high humidities is not so much a property of the material as of its state of aggregation; this view is supported by the fact that the variability is not found when film rather than fibre is studied (*21*).

The immediate consequences of this phenomenon of hysteresis are plain enough. When it is desired to condition a number of samples of unknown prehistory at any given humidity and temperature, for

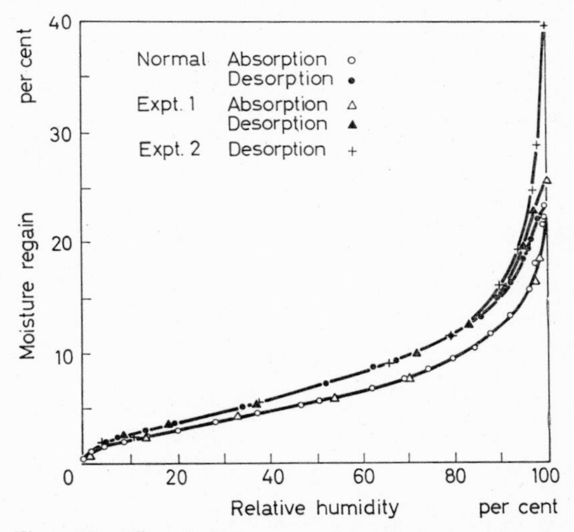

Figure 13. Effect of added water on desorption isotherm for cotton

example, in order to compare their hygroscopicities, inaccurate results will be obtained if the samples are merely introduced into the test atmosphere without regard to their initial condition. It is plain from *Figures 11 and 12* that transition from one boundary curve to the other is effected not by short direct paths, but by long curves similar in shape to the boundary curves themselves. Hence, in order to ensure that all the samples may be in a condition representable by corresponding points on one or other of the boundary curves, before they are conditioned at the test humidity they should come near to equilibrium with an atmosphere as far removed from the test humidity as possible. For example, when it is desired to compare the absorption hygroscopicities of different materials at the temperature and humidity normally used for testing, they should be exposed to an atmosphere of, say, 10% r.h. for at least six hours before they are introduced into the test atmosphere at 65% r.h.

At this stage it is desirable to see if these observations can be fitted into a reasonable explanatory scheme. It was made clear in Chapter 2 that the molecules of most textile fibres contain hydrophilic groups to which water molecules can be bound by means of hydrogen bonds, and it was also explained that in the more crystalline regions of the fibre the molecules are held together laterally by hydrogen bonds between such groups on adjacent molecules. A certain amount of this kind of cross-linking will occur in the amorphous regions also, particularly at the fringes of the crystalline portions. In the cellulosic fibres, with which we are mainly concerned here, the principal hydrophilic groups are the hydroxyl groups of the cellulose molecule, though no doubt the other oxygen-containing groups play a smaller part. This is clear enough from the fact that the hygroscopicity of cellulose is reduced, but not to zero, when all the hydroxyl groups are removed by the formation of appropriate tri-substituted derivatives.

Two additional experimental observations are of value in constructing the theoretical framework. When a sample of cotton is dried for some time at a high temperature (for example, 110°C) its hygroscopicity is reduced (*3*); on the other hand, if it is similarly heated in the presence of a high concentration of water vapour its hygroscopicity may be increased (*22*). It may be assumed for the present that the primary cause of the taking up of water is, as mentioned above, the hydrogen-bonding of water molecules to free hydroxyl groups in the cellulose, though there is little doubt that this simple explanation is complicated by secondary effects. The molecules of cellulose, and, of course, the hydrophilic groups, are in a state of thermal vibration that will increase with increasing temperature; this can result in both the making and the breaking of cross-linking bonds, and the final effect will depend on the amount of water present. Where the amount of water is high, most of the free hydroxyl groups on the cellulose will have water molecules attached to them, and hence the tendency for further cross-linking to occur by mutual satisfaction of hydroxyl groups on adjacent cellulose molecules will be negligible; on the other hand, the breaking of already existing links, which because of the increasing vibration will occur more readily at high temperatures, may easily result in both the groups concerned remaining free, since water molecules will probably attach themselves before recombination becomes possible. The final result is obviously a more-or-less permanent increase in the number of free hydroxyl groups, and hence in the subsequent hygroscopicity of the material. But, if the amount of water present is small, the tendency for additional free groups to be formed will be more than counterbalanced by the tendency for existing free groups to combine with one another, since few of them will have attached water molecules to prevent this occurring. The final result is therefore a permanent decrease of hygroscopicity.

Since heating in a saturated atmosphere increases the hygroscopicity of cotton, and heating in an atmosphere of low humidity decreases it, it is to be expected that at some point between the two extremes no alteration will be produced. The existence of such points is indicated by the intersection (*Figure 9*, p. 19) of the high-temperature isotherms, but it is more instructive to consider these from another point of view. The general effect of increasing the temperature is to decrease the moisture regain of a sample of cotton in equilibrium with an atmosphere of constant relative humidity, as was shown by the curves of *Figure 8*, p. 18, but if the temperature and regain exceed certain values, the increase in the number of available active groups may be sufficient to counterbalance the decrease in the average amount attached to each group, so that the temperature effect seems to reverse. The reversal is therefore essentially due to a change in the material under examination, and there is no need to consider possible failure to conform to thermodynamic deductions.

Now consider the removal of water from a sample of wet fibre—preferably removal effected by putting the sample into a dry atmosphere at room temperature. Initially, all the available hydroxyl groups will have water molecules attached to them, but as the fibre dries these groups will be freed, and there will be a tendency for their residual valencies to be mutually satisfied by hydrogen bonding, involving a certain amount of realignment of the cellulose molecules. This process will go on with increasing difficulty, because of the decrease of swelling and consequent greater difficulty of realigning the molecules, until all the water is removed, and in the process it is to be expected that strains will have been produced in the fibre. The belief that there is a *tendency* for change of configuration to occur does not, however, involve the assumption that it always will occur; some molecules will be held more readily than others, and it may be that a change of configuration is possible only when a loosely bound molecule attains momentarily a sufficiently large amplitude of vibration, so that even the dry material may contain an appreciable number of free hydroxyl groups.

If this material is now allowed to absorb water, the absorption will occur in the first instance on those groups that remain, but the number of groups available for absorption will increase as absorption proceeds, since a proportion of the groups freed by thermal vibration will be prevented from reforming cross-linkages by the speedy attachment to them of water molecules. The number of active groups available during absorption will at any given stage tend to be less than during desorption, because the amplitude of vibration of a molecule held to another by the attraction of one or more active groups will be less than that of a molecule with the active groups free. There is here, therefore, an explanation of hysteresis which postulates that during desorption and absorption the number of active groups concerned in the absorption of water decreases and increases respectively, but with a lag during absorption, so that for the same number of available active groups the humidity will be greater during absorption than during desorption.

This picture provides a reasonable explanation of the effects that have been observed, and in the past has permitted some predictions to be made that were subsequently borne out by experience, but it is far from being the only explanation that has been offered. For example, Barkas (*23*) has propounded a theory in which the hysteresis in moisture absorption is related to a corresponding hysteresis in elastic properties. The deduction of this relation is thermodynamic and its validity is not in question, but it suffers from the defect of all thermodynamic explanations that by their very nature they can reveal nothing of the mechanism involved. It remains to be seen whether it is necessarily incompatible with the mechanistic explanation presented above.

It is now desirable to consider some additional experimental observations, and to see how they fit into the theoretical framework provided. The technical processes normally applied to textile fibres have in general a fairly small effect on their hygroscopicities—with cotton, for example, the differences caused by most processes are smaller than the uncertainties of regain that might be ascribed to unknown differences of prehistory. There is, however, an important exception—processes that involve swelling of the fibre can cause large increases of hygroscopicity. Possibly the most important of these, and certainly that which has received most study, is the process of mercerization. This is carried out by steeping cotton or other cellulosic fibre in a solution of a caustic alkali, the concentration of which must exceed a minimum value determined by the temperature and the particular alkali used. An enormous lateral swelling of the fibre results, and usually the process is conducted in such a way that the accompanying longitudinal shrinkage is either prevented or allowed to occur and then counteracted by stretching, but the most pronounced swelling action is achieved when the fibre is free to change its dimensions without any external restraint.

Figure 14 shows the isotherms (*24*) for samples of loose scoured cotton that had been immersed in (*a*) a 15% solution of caustic soda and (*b*) a 28% solution of caustic potash, and then washed and dried. (The particular concentrations chosen represent corresponding maxima on the swelling curves for the two alkalis.) The isotherm for the original unmercerized cotton is also shown, and it is obvious that a large increase of hygroscopicity has resulted from the treatment. The

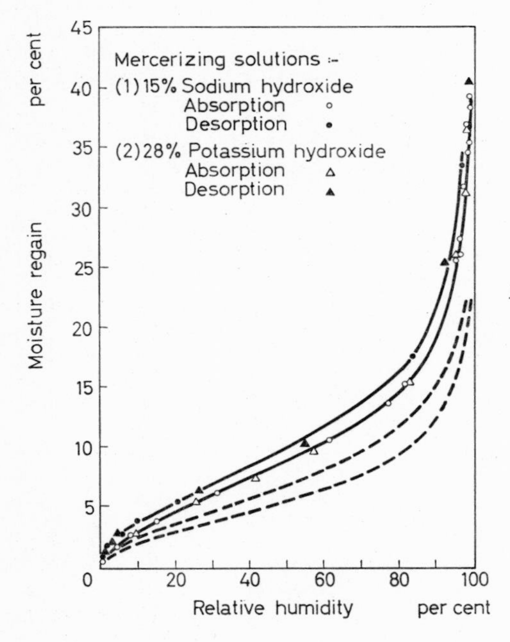

Figure 14. Effect of mercerization on sorption isotherms for loose scoured cotton

general shape of the curves is, however, the same; indeed, Table 4 shows that the ratio of the moisture regain of the mercerized cotton to that of the original scoured cotton is roughly independent of the humidity. It is probable that this is an approximation only—trends are in fact evident from the Table—and it may well be that, as suggested by at least one of the two-phase theories of adsorption, only the closely bound water should demonstrate the constant ratio. For our present purpose, however, the ratios of total water absorbed are sufficiently constant to justify the acceptance of their mean value as a measure of the change in sorptive capacity brought about by the mercerization process. The data for a series of samples mercerized in caustic soda of various concentrations have been similarly examined, and again the value of the mean ratio provides a quantitative description of the change brought about by the process. (Similar ratios for the absorption of substances other than water have since become available (*25–27*), and their value has been well substantiated.) These data are plotted in *Figure 15* against the concentration

TABLE 4

SORPTION OF COTTON MERCERIZED IN 15% SODIUM HYDROXIDE SOLUTION

Relative humidity (%)	Water sorbed (%)					
	Absorption			Desorption		
	Mercerized (*M*)	Scoured (*S*)	Ratio (*M/S*)	Mercerized (*M*)	Scoured (*S*)	Ratio (*M/S*)
5	2·07	1·41	1·47	2·67	1·71	1·56
10	3·00	1·98	1·52	3·66	2·46	1·49
15	3·72	2·46	1·51	4·38	2·97	1·47
20	4·41	2·82	1·56	5·13	3·48	1·47
25	5·07	3·21	1·58	5·88	3·96	1·48
30	5·82	3·66	1·59	6·69	4·50	1·49
35	6·54	4·05	1·62	7·44	4·98	1·49
40	7·23	4·47	1·62	8·22	5·52	1·49
45	7·92	4·92	1·61	9·06	6·06	1·49
50	8·70	5·37	1·62	9·93	6·69	1·48
55	9·45	5·82	1·62	10·74	7·26	1·48
60	10·23	6·30	1·62	11·64	7·92	1·47
65	11·10	6·90	1·61	12·57	8·73	1·44
70	12·06	7·56	1·60	13·62	9·60	1·42
75	13·08	8·31	1·57	14·82	10·53	1·41
80	14·46	9·39	1·54	16·23	11·76	1·38
85	16·20	10·56	1·53	17·97	13·11	1·37
90	18·75	12·30	1·52	21·06	15·00	1·40
95	23·49	15·15	1·55	26·85	18·30	1·47
		Mean = 1·57			Mean = 1·46	

of the mercerizing solution, and it will be noted that the shape of all the regain curves is similar to that of curves relating the swelling of cotton fibres to the concentration of the caustic soda solution in which they were swollen. This was one of the early occasions on which the intimate relation between moisture uptake and swelling was demonstrated.

Swelling is reduced when yarn is mercerized under tension (*28*); this is illustrated by *Figure 16*, which shows that quite a small tension is able to reduce appreciably the moisture sorption ratio and that greater tensions have no greater effect. In one respect the effect of tension is actually greater than that suggested by *Figure 16.* When loose cotton was mercerized without tension the ratios for 15% and

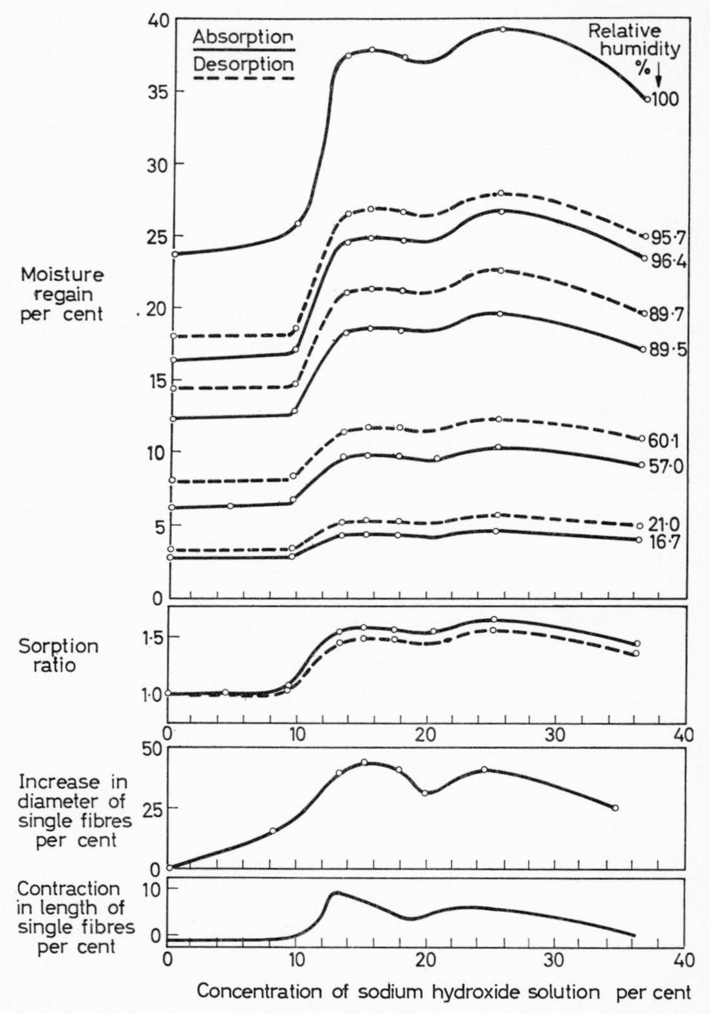

Figure 15. Effect of mercerization on length, diameter, sorption ratio and moisture regain of cotton fibres

25% caustic soda solutions were 1·57 and 1·65, respectively; the corresponding figures for yarn mercerized without tension are here

1·32 and 1·55. It is clear, therefore, that loose yarn in comparison with loose cotton behaves as if it were in fact under slight tension. This is no doubt due to the fact that, when the fibres are twisted together to form a yarn, the free swelling of the individual fibres is to some extent hindered by the constraints imposed on them by their neighbours. This effect is still more evident in the mercerization of fabric (*29*), where the swelling is still further hindered by the interaction of the yarns.

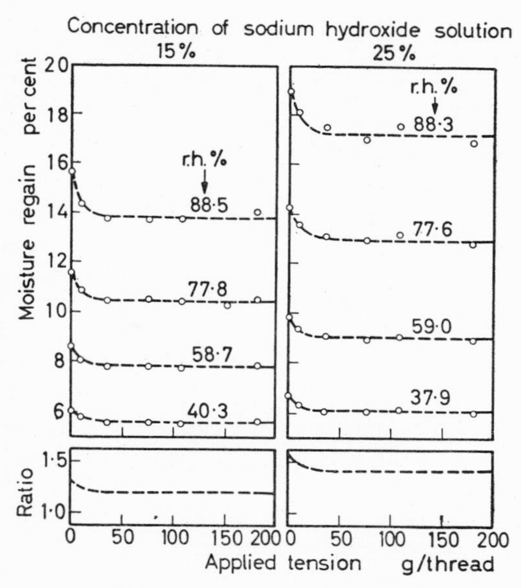

Figure 16. Effect of tension on swelling of cotton fibres during mercerization

It is unnecessary to consider in detail here what happens to the fibres during the mercerization process; it is sufficient to note that, in the very great opening up of the structure that occurs, there is a large increase in the number of hydrophilic groups available for combining with water, dyes, etc. Naturally, the degree of swelling and the water sorption go hand-in-hand, both being due to the same primary cause. In mercerization, particularly of loose cotton, the swelling can be very large, but even so it stops far short of the complete disintegration of the structure that occurs when cellulose is dissolved, when all or nearly all the cross-links may be assumed to be broken. Because of this it would be expected that the number of available hydrophilic groups in a cellulose regenerated from solution would be much greater than in a mercerized cotton, even one produced with maximum swelling. This is, in fact, what is found; the isotherms for viscose and cuprammonium rayons are of the same shape as those for scoured cotton (*21*), and can be obtained from the latter, at least approximately, by multiplying all the regain values by the appropriate sorption ratio. But the actual values of the ratios are greater than have been found for any mercerized cotton, being about 1·8–1·9 for cuprammonium rayon and 1·9–2·0 for ordinary viscose rayon. Even the difference between these is instructive, for cuprammonium rayon

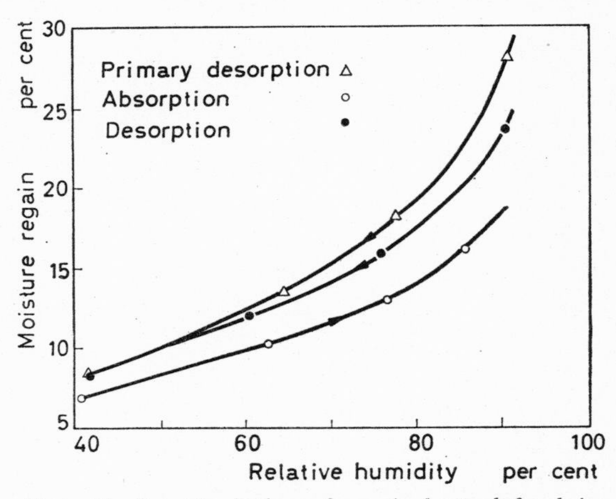

Figure 17. Desorption isotherm of mercerized cotton before drying

is generally spun with greater stretch than viscose, while the imposition of even greater tensions in viscose spinning, as in the production of yarns by the Lilienfeld process, can reduce the ratio to 1·6–1·7. Therefore, from the point of view of sorptive capacity for water, dyes, and the like, the regenerated-cellulose rayons behave as supermercerized cottons.

One other feature calls for mention. During mercerization the degree of swelling is so large that it results in a large increase in the number of available hydrophilic groups, even after the swelling agent has been washed out. This cannot fail to influence hysteresis, if the ideas that have been put forward in explanation of hysteresis bear any relation to the truth. If a sample of cotton after mercerization is washed and its desorption curve is determined directly from the wet condition, the isotherm shown in *Figure 17* is obtained (*8*). From this it is clear that cotton, immediately after being mercerized, and before it has even been air-dried, is capable of holding very large amounts of water. But in this condition the number of available active groups is so large that, as the material is dried, many of them become more or less permanently linked to one another, so that they cease to be available as potential sorbing points. This is no doubt the reason why the uppermost curve of *Figure 17* is an irreproducible primary desorption curve, the subsequent desorption curve obtained after the material has been dried providing evidence of an appreciably impaired sorptive capacity. This kind of effect is found to a smaller extent after kier-boiling, which is a less strongly swelling process,

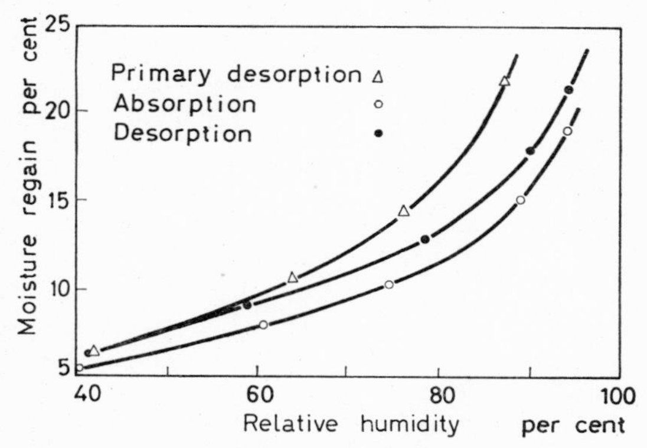

Figure 18. Desorption isotherm of cotton directly after removal from cotton boll

and, as would be expected, to a greater extent in viscose and cuprammonium yarns and fibres before their first drying. It is also seen, probably to its maximum extent (*Figure 18*), in cotton taken from the cotton boll before the sun has been able to dry it out. The cellulose in cotton fibre is laid down from solution, and hence is born with its hydrophilic groups attached to water molecules, so that there is ample opportunity for cross-linking to occur during the primary drying.

As mentioned at the beginning, this chapter has been very largely confined to cellulosic fibres. The general principles underlying the sorption process are, however, the same for all fibres, and it seemed more profitable in a work of this kind to discuss a few selected topics in reasonable detail rather than deal somewhat superficially with all the features that would have to be included in a complete survey covering all the important fibres. It is hoped that the very limitations imposed by this method of treatment will assist rather than hinder the reader to extend his basic knowledge in whatever direction he may desire.

REFERENCES

1 H. B. Bull, *J. Amer. Chem. Soc.*, **66,** 1499 (1944).
2 A. F. Mellon, A. H. Korn and S. R. Hoover, *J. Amer. Chem. Soc.*, **69,** 827 (1947); **70,** 114 (1948).
3 A. R. Urquhart and A. M. Williams, *J. Text. Inst.*, **15,** T138 (1924).
4 S. W. Benson, D. A. Ellis and R. W. Zwanzig, *J. Amer. Chem. Soc.*, **72,** 2102 (1950).
5 J. W. McBain and A. M. Bakr, *J. Amer. Chem. Soc.*, **48,** 690 (1926).
6 J. W. McBain, S. J. Good, A. M. Bakr, D. P. Davies, H. J. Willavoys and R. Buckingham, *Trans. Faraday Soc.*, **29,** 1086 (1933).
7 S. L. Madorsky, *Rev. Sci. Instrum.*, **21,** 393 (1950).
8 P. M. Hauser and A. D. McLaren, *Industr. Engng Chem.*, **40,** 112 (1948).
9 D. K. Ashpole, *Proc. Roy. Soc.*, **A212,** 112 (1952).
10 J. B. Speakman, *J. Soc. Chem. Ind.*, **49,** T209 (1930).
11 A. R. Urquhart and A. M. Williams, *J. Text. Inst.*, **15,** T433 (1924).
12 J. B. Taylor, *J. Text. Inst.*, **43,** T489 (1952).
13 J. B. Taylor, *J. Text. Inst.*, **45,** T642 (1954).
14 S. Brunauer, *Physical Adsorption of Gases and Vapours*, Oxford University Press, 1943, pp. 149 *et seq.*
15 F. T. Peirce, *J. Text. Inst.*, **20,** T133 (1929).
16 A. J. Hailwood and S. Horrobin, *Trans. Faraday Soc.*, **42B**, 84 (1946).
17 A. R. Urquhart and A. M. Williams, *J. Text. Inst.*, **15,** T559 (1924).
18 J. B. Speakman and C. A. Cooper, *J. Text. Inst.*, **27,** T191 (1936).
19 A. R. Urquhart, unpublished.
20 A. R. Urquhart and N. Eckersall, *J. Text. Inst.*, **21,** T499 (1930).
21 A. R. Urquhart and N. Eckersall, *J. Text. Inst.*, **23,** T163 (1932).
22 A. R. Urquhart, *J. Text. Inst.*, **20,** T125 (1929).
23 W. W. Barkas, *The Swelling of Wood under Stress*, H.M.S.O., 1949.
24 A. R. Urquhart and A. M. Williams, *J. Text. Inst.*, **16,** T155 (1925)
25 S. M. Neale, *J. Text. Inst.*, **22,** T320 (1931).
26 S. M. Neale, *J. Text. Inst.*, **22,** T349 (1931).
27 T. Brownsett, F. D. Farrow and S. M. Neale, *J. Text. Inst.*, **22,** T357 (1931).
28 A. R. Urquhart, *J. Text. Inst.*, **18,** T55 (1927).
29 A. R. Urquhart and N. Eckersall, *J. Text. Inst.*, **23,** T135 (1932).

CHAPTER 4

HEAT OF ABSORPTION

By W. H. Rees

The absorption of moisture by textiles is an exothermic process. The amount of heat evolved depends upon (*a*) the nature of the absorbent, (*b*) the amount of moisture present in the absorbent prior to absorption (i.e., its moisture regain), (*c*) the amount of moisture absorbed, and (*d*) whether the moisture is absorbed from the liquid or from the vapour phase.

However, before discussing this subject in any detail it is advisable to define the thermal quantities involved. The thermal changes that accompany the absorption of moisture by hygroscopic materials may be expressed in several ways. This has led to confusion in the literature, since different authors have given various titles to the same heat quantity, and hence, to avoid ambiguity, the possible ways of expressing the quantities of heat evolved when a fibre absorbs or is wetted by water are given in Table 5.

The term 'heat of swelling' is surely a misnomer, since the swelling is not responsible for the evolution of the heat, but is merely another consequence of the absorption of water. Furthermore, the thermal effect is greatest when the swelling is least, and vice-versa.

INTER-RELATIONSHIP OF THE THERMAL QUANTITIES

It is theoretically possible to carry out experiments in more than one way, e.g., water may be absorbed either from the vapour or from the liquid, and the differences in heat evolved must be the latent heat of condensation of water vapour, i.e.,

$$Q_v = Q_L + L \qquad \ldots.(1)$$

where L is the latent heat of condensation of water vapour (582 cal/g at 25°C).

Similarly,

$$H_v = H_L + \alpha L \qquad \ldots.(2)$$

where α is the fractional moisture regain.

Since integral heats are additive, the heat evolved when the fibre is immersed in liquid water will be the same as it would be in a two-stage process in which the fibre absorbed sufficient liquid water to

TABLE 5

Accepted Title	Definition of Quantity: Heat Evolved	Definitive Symbol	Symbol Used in Text	Units	Other Published Titles for Quantity
Differential Heat of Absorption of liquid water	By infinite mass of material at moisture regain α on absorbing unit mass of liquid water	Q_L^{α}	Q_L	Calories per gram of liquid water	Differential Heat of Swelling Differential Heat of Sorption Differential Heat of Absorption Heat of Absorption
Differential Heat of Absorption of water vapour	By infinite mass of material at moisture regain α on absorbing unit mass of water vapour	Q_v^{α}	Q_v	Calories per gram of water vapour	Differential Heat of Sorption Heat of Absorption
Integral Heat of Absorption of liquid water	By dry material on absorbing sufficient liquid water to raise its moisture regain from zero to α	$H_L^{0-\alpha}$	H_L	Calories per gram of dry material	Integral Heat of Swelling Integral Heat of Absorption Heat of Absorption
Integral Heat of Absorption of water vapour	By dry material on absorbing sufficient water vapour to raise its moisture regain from zero to α	$H_v^{0-\alpha}$	H_v	Calories per gram of dry material	Integral Heat of Sorption Integral Heat of Absorption
Heat of Wetting	By dry material on absorbing very large quantity of liquid water	$H_L^{0-\infty}$	$\overline{W}$	Calories per gram of dry material	Heat of Soaking Integral Heat of Sorption
Heat of Wetting	By material at moisture regain α on absorbing very large quantity of liquid water	$H_L^{\alpha-\infty}$	W	Calories per gram of dry material	Heat of Soaking Integral Heat of Sorption

reach a regain α, after which it was put into liquid water. Expressed in terms of symbols,

$$H_L^{0-\alpha}+H_L^{\alpha-\infty} = H_L^{0-\infty}$$

i.e.,

$$H_L+W=\bar{W} \quad \text{or, } H_L = \bar{W}-W \qquad \ldots.(3)$$

In other words, the integral heat of absorption of liquid water to the regain α is equal to the difference between the heat of wetting of the dry material and the heat of wetting of the material at the regain α.

The differential heats of absorption, Q_L and Q_v, are not quantities that can be readily measured, and the heats of wetting, $\bar{W}$ and W, are more convenient quantities for experimental measurement. The relation between W and Q_L can be readily established as follows.

If a mass of material whose dry weight is 1 gram and fractional moisture regain is α has its regain increased to $\alpha+\mathrm{d}\alpha$, where $\mathrm{d}\alpha$ is a very small amount of added water, the heat evolved is $Q_L.\mathrm{d}\alpha$. We may consider the complete wetting to be carried out in stages so that the total heat evolved is the sum of such terms as $Q_L.\mathrm{d}\alpha$ carried as far as saturation. The heat of wetting per gram of dry material is thus given by

$$W = \int_{\alpha}^{\alpha_s} Q_L.\mathrm{d}\alpha \qquad \ldots.(4)$$

where α_s is the saturation moisture regain. It follows that

$$Q_L = -\frac{\mathrm{d}W}{\mathrm{d}\alpha} \qquad \ldots.(5)$$

The heat of absorption of liquid water at any moisture regain of the material may thus be derived from the slope of the experimentally determined curve relating W and α. Conversely, from the curve relating Q_L and α, the heat of wetting of the dry material is represented by the area contained by the ordinate corresponding to the initial moisture regain, the curve and the regain axis.

It follows from equations (3) and (5) that

$$Q_L = +\frac{\mathrm{d}H_L}{\mathrm{d}\alpha} \qquad \ldots.(6)$$

Thus Q_L may also be obtained from the slope of the curve relating integral heats of absorption of liquid water and the moisture regain.

INTERPRETATION OF THE THERMAL QUANTITIES

The differential heat of absorption is a measure of the heat that must be added to the molecules of absorbed moisture in order that they will have sufficient energy to break away from the attraction of the absorbent. Thus, the differential heat of absorption gives an indication of the strength of the bond between the molecules of the absorbate and the absorbent; for example, in the primary absorption of water by native cellulose, of the strength of the bond between the water molecules and the hydroxyl groups in the amorphous regions of the cellulose molecular structure, the hydroxyl groups in the crystalline regions not being accessible to water. The heat of wetting, on the other hand, will depend to a large extent upon the availability of the hydroxyl groups or, in other words, upon the proportion of amorphous material present in the molecular structure of a particular type of cellulose. Thus, information of a fundamental nature may be obtained from a knowledge of the heat exchanges occurring in the absorption of moisture by textile materials.

METHODS FOR EVALUATING THE THERMAL QUANTITIES

There are two distinct lines of attack, namely,

(*a*) the direct or calorimetric method for evaluating heats of wetting and integral heats of absorption, and

(*b*) the indirect or isosteric method for evaluating differential heats of absorption, i.e., by thermodynamical calculation from absorption–temperature relations.

They will be considered in turn.

(*a*) *Calorimetric method*

The heat of wetting is determined by measuring the temperature rise when a mass of textile material, previously conditioned to a known moisture regain, is introduced into water contained in a calibrated calorimeter. The integral heat is more complex but may be determined by feeding moisture on to the textile material from a closed system. The technique demands precision, since the apparatus required for such experimental work on bulky textile materials has a large thermal capacity, so that the observed rises in temperature are small. Some workers (*1*, *2*) have used adiabatic calorimeters for this purpose, but more generally a non-adiabatic method has been employed and cooling corrections then have to be applied.

Figure 19 shows diagrammatically the apparatus used by Rees (*3*) and Guthrie (*4*) for measuring heats of wetting of cellulose. It consists of a pair of Dewar flasks, each of 540 cm^3 capacity, with a copper–Constantan thermocouple system arranged to operate differentially between them. A stirrer and heater system is supplied for each flask, as well as a specially designed glass container, fitted with a water-tight aluminium stopper, in which the previously conditioned test specimens are placed. 200 cm^3 of distilled water are placed in each flask and, after temperature equilibrium has been established, the specimen in one of the flasks is released from its container and wetted, the resulting temperature rise being estimated from the deflection of the galvanometer incorporated in the thermocouple circuit. A temperature rise of 0·0001°C is detectable, and the values observed during the experiments ranged from about 0·01 to about 0·4°C. The water-equivalent of the system is determined in a separate experiment by

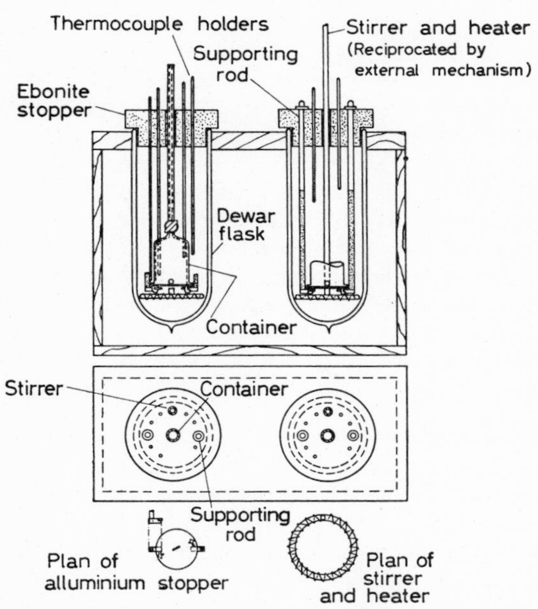

Figure 19. Apparatus for measuring heats of wetting of cellulose

introducing a certain quantity of water and dissipating a known quantity of electrical energy from the heater.

The heat of wetting (W) of a specimen is calculated from the expression:

$$W = \frac{IVt}{4 \cdot 18m} \times \frac{d_1}{d_2} \qquad \ldots .(7)$$

where V is the potential drop across the heater (in volts), t is the time (in seconds) that current I (amps) passes through the heater, m is the dry-weight of the specimen (in grams), and d_1 and d_2 are the corrected galvanometer deflections for the wetting and electrical heating parts of the experiment, respectively.

The moisture regain of the specimen is found from its conditioned weight before wetting and its dry-weight, the latter being determined after the completion of the calorimetric experiment. For such a calorimeter the estimated experimental accuracy is $\pm 0{\cdot}5\%$. For full details of the apparatus and its manipulation, the reader is referred to the original publication by Rees (*3*).

Wahba (*5*) has used a similar technique for measuring the heat of wetting of cellulose, his apparatus differing only in detail from that described above. Wahba used one Dewar flask only, with the cellulose specimen enclosed in a glass ampoule whose capillary end was broken under the water at the start of the experiment, the resulting temperature rise being measured by a Beckmann thermometer.

Newsome and Sheppard (*6*) have used a similar type of apparatus for measuring the integral heat of absorption of water vapour by cellulose acetate film. The fragmented film was contained in a bulb connected to a vacuum system, and, on allowing small quantities of water to be evaporated in the system, the rise in temperature in the calorimeter and the corresponding equilibrium vapour pressure were observed. After the re-establishment of equilibrium, a further small quantity of moisture was introduced into the system, and the procedure repeated.

(*b*) *Isosteric method*

Shorter (*7*) has applied thermodynamical reasoning to the problem of the absorption of moisture by textile materials, making use of the Kirchoff equation for the heat of dilution of a solution. This is derived from the Clausius–Clapeyron equation and can be applied to any two-phase system in which matter is transferred from one phase to the other by a reversible process.

Shorter's derived equation for the absorption of moisture by a textile material is

$$Q_L = \left(\frac{RT^2 \mathrm{d}\log_e h}{M \quad \mathrm{d}T}\right)_\alpha \qquad \ldots.(8)$$

where Q_L is the differential heat of absorption of liquid water by the textile material at moisture regain α at the absolute temperature T in equilibrium with the relative humidity h, R being the gas constant and M the molecular weight of water.

Equation (8) may be rewritten as follows:

$$Q_L = -\frac{R}{M} \cdot \frac{\mathrm{d}(\log_e h)}{\mathrm{d}(1/T)} \qquad \ldots.(9)$$

Thus, if a moisture regain α is maintained by a relative humidity h_1 at an absolute temperature T_1, and by a relative humidity h_2 at a temperature T_2, equation (9) gives, by the substitution of finite for infinitesimal increments,

$$Q_L = \frac{RT_1 T_2}{M} \cdot \frac{(\log_e h_2 - \log_e h_1)}{(T_2 - T_1)} \quad \ldots . (10)$$

Hence, from a knowledge of the variation of $\log_e h$ with $1/T$ for a given moisture regain, the value of Q_L may be calculated by means of equation (10). Such absorption data for soda-boiled cotton have been given by Urquhart and Williams (*8*). These authors give isosteres, where log(vapour pressure) is plotted against $1/T$, so that equation (10) can be readily applied.

For equation (10) to be strictly valid, Q_L should not vary between the temperatures T_1 and T_2, and the absorption process should be reversible. That the process is not reversible is shown by the familiar hysteresis effect, and it is a debatable point as to which values of moisture regain ought to be used in the calculation. However, equation (10) has been applied widely to calculate values of Q_L from absorption data.

EXPERIMENTAL RESULTS AND DISCUSSION

(*a*) *Integral heats of absorption*

Figure 20 shows graphically the experimental relationship obtained by Newsome and Sheppard (*6*) between the integral heat of absorp-

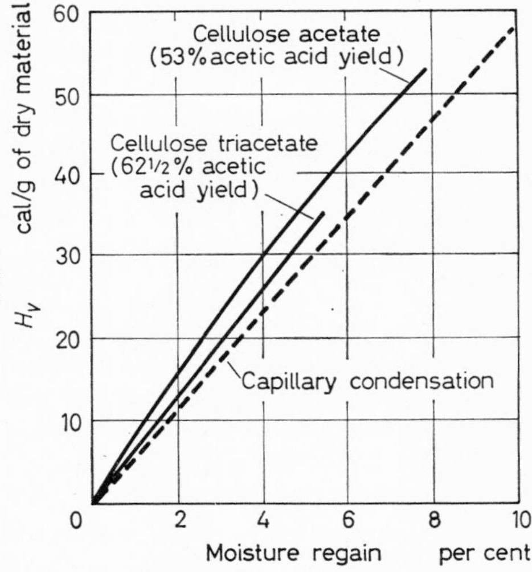

Figure 20. Integral heat of absorption of water vapour and moisture regain for two types of cellulose acetate

tion of water vapour and the moisture regain for two types of cellulose acetate, namely a normal secondary acetate (53% acetic acid yield), and fully acetylated cellulose, i.e., cellulose triacetate ($62\frac{1}{2}$% acetic acid yield), along with a theoretical curve based on pure capillary condensation. The following conclusions may be drawn:

(1) The heat evolved on the absorption of moisture by the acetate materials is greater than that due to condensation of water vapour in the capillary systems of the cellulose materials, indicating that inter-molecular forces operate between the absorbate and the absorbent in the absorption process.

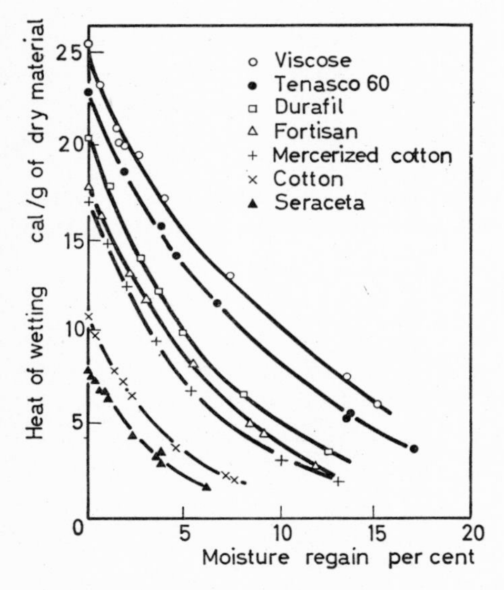

Figure 21. Heat of wetting and moisture regain for cellulosic fibres

(2) The heat liberated by the triacetate is less than that liberated by the absorption of the same amount of water by the normal acetate, the former being nearer to the capillary condensation curve. Acetylation of the free hydroxyl groups in the cellulose structure reduces the affinity between them and the water molecules; with fully acetylated cellulose there are no free hydroxyl groups, and the absorption process approaches that of capillary condensation.

Rees (*3*) and Guthrie (*4*) have measured the heats of wetting in water of eighteen types of cellulosic fibre at moisture regains corresponding to relative humidities ranging from zero to approximately 70%, and selected experimental results are shown in *Figure 21.* All measurements were made on samples which had been conditioned from zero regain to their final value.

The following conclusions are drawn from this work:

(1) The heats of wetting of the various cellulosic materials are greatest at dryness and decrease with increasing moisture regain.

(2) The heats of wetting for a sample with a given moisture regain increase with increasing hygroscopicity of the cellulosic materials. Roughly, the heat of wetting at dryness for regenerated cellulose is about twice the corresponding value for native cellulose. Thus, heats of wetting yield information regarding the relative amounts of water-binding material in the different fibres, the amount being greater for regenerated and mercerized cellulose than for native cellulose, and less for acetylated cellulose, which is in accord with the relative hygroscopicities of these materials.

Effect of stretching—If, during the manufacture of regenerated cellulose, the material is stretch-spun, which is common practice in

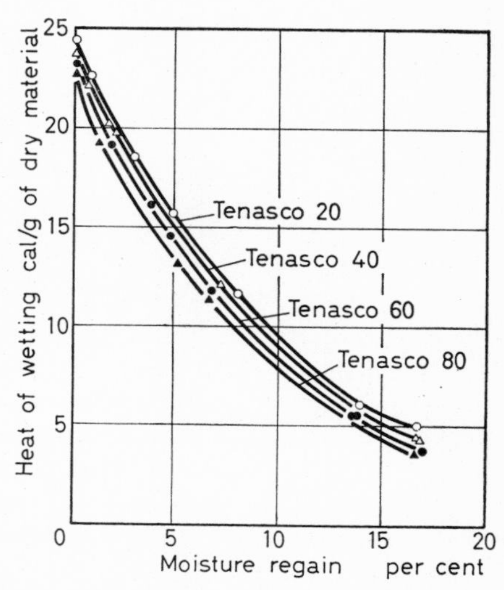

Figure 22. Effect of stretching on relation between heat of wetting and moisture regain
(By courtesy of *J. Text. Inst.*, 1949)

the production of high-tenacity rayons, the degree of orientation of the chain molecules will increase with the degree of stretching applied. If it be assumed that an increase in the degree of molecular orientation results in an increase in the degree of crystallinity and therefore in a decrease in the proportion of amorphous, or water-binding, material in the cellulose structure, then the heats of wetting would be expected to decrease with increasing degree of stretching applied in the spinning process. This effect is illustrated in *Figure 22*, taken from

Guthrie's paper (*4*). The decrease in the heat of wetting with increasing stretch is consistent with the decrease in the hygroscopicity of the fibres, the latter being 15·4, 14·9, 14·5 and 13·8% for Tenasco of 20, 40, 60 and 80% stretch, respectively, at 65% relative humidity and 25°C.

Hysteresis effect—Argue and Maass (*1*) have measured the heat of wetting of purified cotton cellulose after conditioning to various moisture regains (*a*) by absorption and (*b*) by partial desorption from saturation. Some of their results are given in Table 6.

TABLE 6

Moisture regain (%)	Head of wetting (cal/g)	
	Absorption	Desorption
0	10·16	—
1	8·0	9·29
3	4·9	5·32
5	2·98	3·20
7	1·99	2·17

The data show that the thermal effect is greater for cellulose containing a given amount of moisture as a result of partial desorption than for cellulose containing the same amount of moisture acquired by absorption. This difference is attributed by Argue and Maass to the larger surface available in the cellulose conditioned by desorption compared with the cellulose conditioned by adsorption.

Temperature effect—All the experimental results quoted hitherto have been obtained at a temperature of 25°C. Wahba and Nashed (*9*) have measured the heat of wetting of dry cellulose at various temperatures within the range 0–40°C, and have found that the heat of wetting decreases linearly with increasing temperature with a coefficient of 0·042 cal/°C/g cellulose.

Non-cellulosic fibres—Published information for non-cellulosic fibres is scanty. Hedges (*10*) has measured calorimetrically the heat of wetting of wool and of silk at various moisture regains, and the heats of wetting of silk fibroin initially containing various amounts of water have been measured calorimetrically by Dunford and Morrison (*2*). The following values for the dry material are quoted here to indicate the order of magnitude of the thermal effects for wool and silk in comparison with those for certain cellulosic fibres given in *Figure 21*, p. 40:

Wool $\bar{W} = 24 \cdot 1$ cal/g (direct determination (*10*))
Silk $\bar{W} \fallingdotseq 16$ cal/g (extrapolated value (*10*))
$\bar{W} = 15 \cdot 93$ cal/g (direct determination (*2*))

Using the apparatus illustrated in *Figure 19*, p. 37, the present author (*11*) obtained a value of 15·0 cal/g for the heat of wetting in water of degummed China silk at zero regain.

Speakman and Saville (*12*) have calculated heats of absorption for nylon by the isosteric method, from which data the present author has calculated the heat of wetting at dryness. The value obtained for drawn nylon was 7·5 cal/g, but this should be accepted only as an order of magnitude of the thermal effect for reasons which will be stated later.

(*b*) *Differential heats of absorption*

(*i*) *Derived from the experimental data of heat of wetting*—Values of the heat of absorption of liquid water at various moisture regains were derived by Rees (*3*) and Guthrie (*4*) from the slopes of tangents to the experimental curves relating heat of wetting and moisture regain, according to equation (5). A polynomial relating heat evolved to moisture regain was fitted to the experimental results near the origin of the curve and the slopes were determined by differentiation. At higher values of moisture regain the slopes of the tangents were measured directly by means of a slope-meter. The reason for adopting these different procedures is that the latter method becomes inaccurate at the lower regain values, where the slope of the curve is steepest, owing to possible slight errors in drawing the curve near the origin.

Figure 23, taken from the paper by Rees (*3*), shows the derived curves relating Q_L and moisture regain for various cellulosic fibres; similar curves for other cellulosic fibres have been published by Guthrie (*4*). The most striking feature of these results is the approximate equality of the Q_L values for the dry materials. The mean figure for all the values derived by Rees and by Guthrie at dryness is 294 cal/g of liquid water absorbed, i.e., 876 cal/g of water vapour (15·7 kcal/mol of water vapour). The constancy of Q_L at zero moisture regain for the eighteen types of cellulosic fibres examined indicates that the *nature* of the absorbing matter in the cellulose structure is identical in all the materials examined, and it seems reasonable to suggest that this is true for all types of cellulose, the *amount* of absorbing matter varying from one material to another as indicated by their different heats of wetting.

In *Figure 23*, values of Q_L have been plotted against corresponding values of moisture regain, but if the nature of the absorbing matter of all cellulosic fibres is the same, values of Q_L plotted against corresponding values of relative humidity should yield the same curve for all the fibres. This has been pointed out by Babbitt (*13*) and by Guthrie (*4*), and from the combined results of Rees and Guthrie a mean curve has been derived representing the variation of heat of absorption with relative humidity for cellulosic fibres. This curve will be referred to later.

Figure 23 shows that the differential heat of absorption decreases rapidly with increasing moisture regain of the cellulose, for beyond the primary stage of absorption secondary linkages are formed between the water molecules already linked with the hydroxyl groups of the cellulose and the incoming molecules, resulting in a lowering of the bond energy.

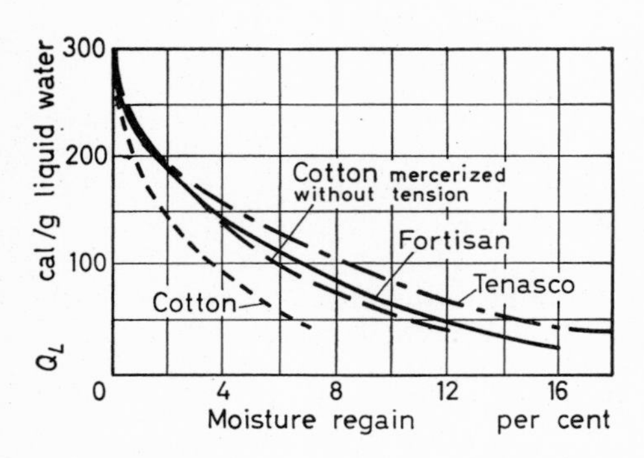

Figure 23. Differential heat of absorption of water and moisture regain for cellulosic fibres

Since the heat evolved per gram of liquid water absorbed at dryness is of the same order for all the cellulosic fibres, it would be expected that the heat evolved per gram of fibre would be proportional to the moisture regain of the fibre. This is illustrated in *Figure 24*. The H_L values were calculated by means of equation (3) from data by Rees (*3*) and Guthrie (*4*). The abscissæ of the points on each curve are the moisture regains of the various fibres at a relative humidity of 65%. It is seen that all the points lie on a straight line.

In this connection, Wahba (*14*), experimenting with viscose rayon and standard cellulose, found that the average value of the sorption ratio for these materials (i.e., the ratio of the moisture regain of viscose rayon to the moisture regain of standard cellulose at a given relative humidity) from near-dryness to saturation was 1·86, and that the corresponding average ratio for the integral heats of absorption of liquid water was 1·87, which again supports the proportionality concept.

The hypothesis that the nature of the absorbing matter of all cellulosic fibres is the same may be tested as follows. If it is true, then the co-ordinates of points on the curves relating heat of wetting and moisture regain (examples of which are given in *Figure 21*, p. 40) should differ in scale only, and so, by applying a factor to both co-ordinates of all points on the curve for one type of cellulosic fibre, it should be possible to cause the curve to coincide with that for another type of cellulosic fibre. Guthrie (*4*) has done this for all the fibres for which he has measured the heat of wetting, ranging from viscose ($\bar{W}=25{\cdot}2$ cal/g) to Seraceta ($\bar{W}=8{\cdot}2$ cal/g), with Sea Island

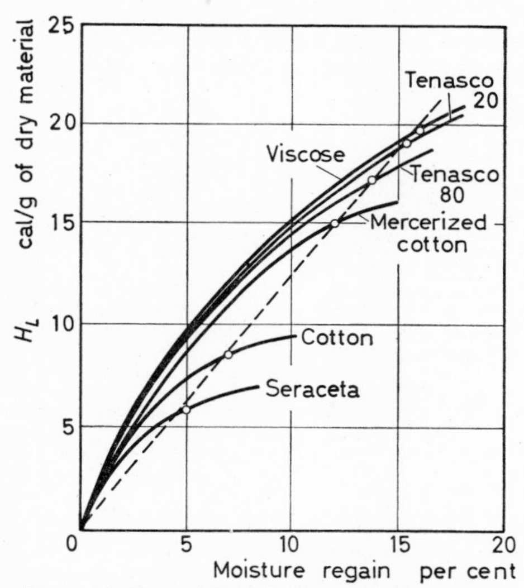

Figure 24. Integral heat of absorption of liquid water and moisture regain for cellulosic fibres

cotton ($\bar{W}=11{\cdot}2$ cal/g) taken as the reference. The result is shown in *Figure 25*. It is clear that all the points lie near to a single curve and that the hypothesis is supported.

(*ii*) *Derived from moisture absorption data*—The heat of absorption can be derived from isosteres by applying equation (10), as has been done by Rees (*3*), using the data of Urquhart and Williams (*8*) for soda-boiled cotton. Similar calculations have been made from the same absorption data by several other workers, and the values obtained are plotted in *Figure 26*.

It is apparent that the values calculated by the various workers are not in good agreement. This indicates the inaccuracy of the isosteric method for evaluating differential heats of absorption. The calculated values depend greatly on the accuracy with which the isosteres are drawn, and further, since the lowest moisture regain given by

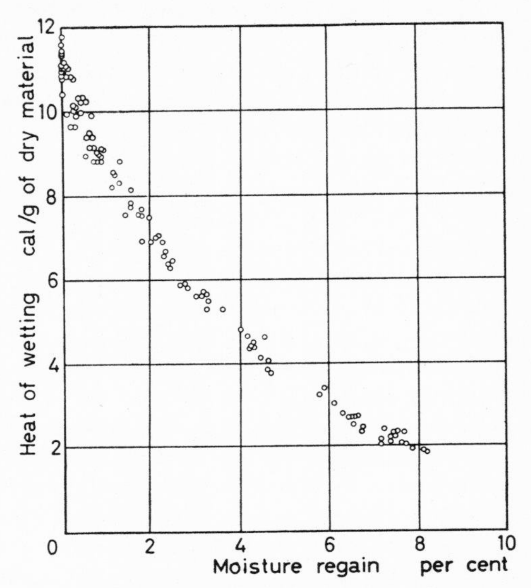

Figure 25. Heat of wetting and moisture regain for cellulosic fibres

(By courtesy of *J. Text. Inst.*, 1949)

Urquhart and Williams is 1·2%, the heat of absorption at zero moisture regain cannot be accurately estimated, as it involves a long

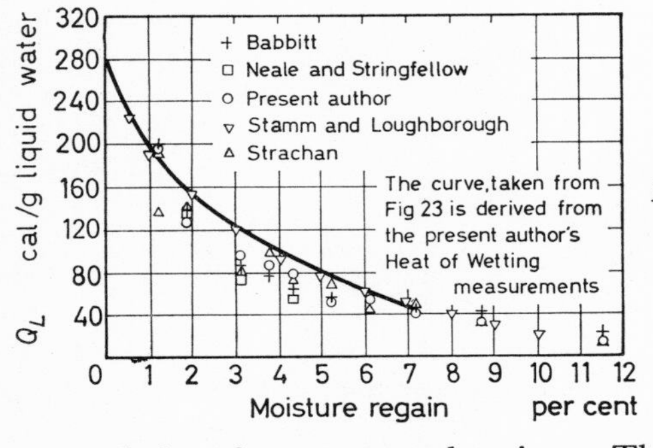

Figure 26. Calculated values of differential heat of absorption

extrapolation from scattered points. The value of Q_L at zero moisture regain estimated by graphical extrapolation from the values calculated by Rees is about 340 cal/g, whereas Babbitt (*13*), from his calculated values from the same source, estimated it to be about 280 cal/g. The value of 340 cal/g is appreciably higher than that (285 cal/g) derived by Rees (*3*) from experimentally determined heats of wetting of cotton.

A further example of the discrepancy between the values of Q_L derived by the two methods is provided by Newsome and Sheppard (*6*), who obtained a value of about 260 cal/g of liquid water for cellulose acetate at zero moisture regain from their calorimetric data, whereas the value derived by the isosteric method was roughly double this figure.

Taylor has calculated the differential heats of absorption of water by a commercial viscose rayon (*15*) and by cotton (*16*) by applying the isosteric method to his own observations of the sorption of water by these materials at low humidities. Extrapolation of his calculated data to zero regain yields values for Q_L at dryness of about 305 cal/g for viscose rayon and about 360 cal/g for cotton. Taylor concludes that the value of Q_v differs slightly for absorption-conditioned and desorption-conditioned material, for both native and regenerated cellulose, Q_v being higher for the desorption-conditioned material.

It will be obvious that calculation by means of equation (4) of the heat of wetting from values of the heat of absorption derived by the isosteric method will be only approximate, as the area under the curve relating heat of absorption and moisture regain must be estimated, and this curve cannot be plotted with much accuracy from the calculated values. For example, Strachan (*17*) calculated heats of absorption from the data of Urquhart and Williams and derived a value of 5·6 cal/g of cotton for the heat of wetting at dryness; the value found by Rees from Strachan's calculated heats of absorption is 8·2 cal/g, and that calculated by Rees from his heat of absorption values derived from the data of Urquhart and Williams is 9·6 cal/g. These three widely differing values are all calculated from the same absorption data.

The calculation of heats of absorption by the isosteric method is inaccurate for the following reasons:

(1) Inaccuracy in plotting the isosteres, which are not always strictly linear.

(2) The assumption made in the derivation of equation (10) that Q_L is independent of temperature may not be strictly true.

(3) The thermodynamical equation (10) should be applied only to a reversible process, which the absorption of moisture by textile fibres is not.

HEAT EXCHANGES AND THE MECHANICAL PROPERTIES OF FIBRES

Ashpole (*18*) has made a statistical analysis of the heat of wetting data of Rees (*3*) and Guthrie (*4*), utilizing an empirical relationship of linearity between log W and moisture regain. According to this, the differential heats of absorption of the various cellulosic fibres at dryness show significant differences; the fibres that have the highest differential heats of absorption at zero regain are those with heats of wetting intermediate among those of the cellulose fibres. No comment is made on the significance of this deduction.

Ashpole's values of differential heats of absorption at zero regain, calculated from the data of Rees and Guthrie on the basis of his empirical relationship, are given in Table 7 along with those derived by Rees and by Guthrie by the method described on p. 43.

TABLE 7

No. in Fig. 27	Fibre	Q_L at zero regain (cal/g)		Initial Young's modulus (g/den)
		From Ashpole's analysis	From Rees and Guthrie	
1	Seraceta (cellulose acetate)	204	295	27
2	Bengals cotton	232	317	44
9	Viscose rayon	219	280	51
8	Tenasco (strong viscose)	240	291	68
7	Cuprammonium rayon	266	290	68
6	Fibro (viscose staple)	244	290	74
3	Sea Island cotton	243	295	82
–	Mercerized cotton (under tension)	293	282	162
5	Durafil (very strong viscose of high orientation)	293	296	176
–	Fortisan (strong saponified acetate)	295	279	183
4	Flax	288	298	203

Large discrepancies are observed between the values derived by Rees and by Guthrie and most of those recalculated by Ashpole. Whereas Ashpole's values are calculated from a linear relationship between log W and moisture regain applied to the whole range of regain values used in the experiments, the values given by Rees and by Guthrie are calculated from experimental data for W restricted to samples of low moisture regain which, in their experience, yield the more accurate experimental data for W.

Also given in Table 7 are values of the initial Young's modulus of the fibres, due mainly to Meredith (*19*); Ashpole notes a close correspondence between them and his recalculated differential heats of absorption at zero regain. The correlation coefficient is found to be 0·928, which is highly significant, and is explained by Ashpole in terms of the structure of the fibres, as follows. The differential heat of absorption at zero regain is a measure of the freedom of the hydrogen bonds associated with the hydroxyl groups in the amorphous regions of the fibre structure, high values implying high hydrogen-bond energy. The amorphous region is also responsible for the strength of the fibre (the strength of a chain being that of its weakest link). It is the hydrogen bonds in this region that are thought to hold the fibre together when it is stretched. Ashpole comments that the high correlation between Q_L at zero regain and the initial Young's modulus presents evidence for this picture of the molecular structure and its relation to fibre strength, and concludes from this that, for the initial strains with all cellulose fibres, it is the hydrogen bonds which yield. The present writer doubts the validity of this conclusion for the following reasons:

(*a*) The initial Young's modulus of Sea Island cotton is roughly twice that of Bengals cotton. This, however, is mainly due to the different spiral angles of the cellulose chain molecules in the two cottons, that is, to the different morphological structures of the fibres, and can be explained without reference to hydrogen bonding.

(*b*) Amongst the regenerated cellulose fibres quoted, the increase in initial Young's modulus from viscose through Tenasco, Fibro and Durafil to Fortisan is known to be correlated with the orientation of the cellulose chain molecules as shown by X-rays. It is conceivable that the hydrogen bonds in the more highly oriented fibres have higher energies, but it does not follow from these observations that the higher hydrogen-bond energy is the *cause* of the higher modulus.

(*c*) With regard to Seraceta (cellulose acetate), the fact that the *density* of hydrogen bonds in its molecular structure is considerably less than the density in regenerated cellulose can account for the lower modulus of the cellulose acetate without assuming different values for the energy content per bond.

In *Figure 27*, Ashpole has plotted the heat of wetting at zero regain against the work of rupture for the various fibres. He comments that some correspondence is noted, provided that the points for Sea Island cotton and cellulose acetate are ignored. On the molecular picture given above, correlation between these two variables would not be expected unless the hydrogen bonding was largely responsible for the entire stress–strain curve. The divergence for the cotton is loosely explained by Ashpole in terms of its spiral morphological structure, and for the cellulose acetate by the preponderance of acetyl over hydrogen bonds in its molecular structure. Ashpole concludes that the hydrogen bonds are largely responsible for the strength of the fibre right up to the breaking point, except for Sea Island cotton and cellulose acetate, the other structures of which predominate after the initial strain.

The present writer feels, however, that the correspondence noted by Ashpole between the heat of wetting at zero regain of the various

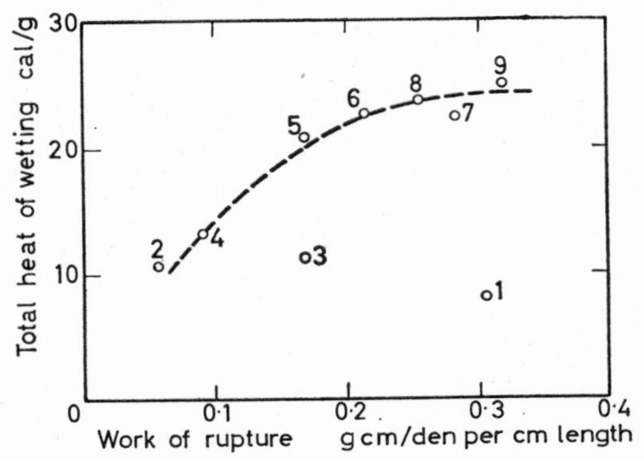

Figure 27. Heat of wetting and work of rupture for cellulosic fibres (see Table 7, p. 48 for key to numbers)

cellulose fibres and their work of rupture may be related to the fact that fibres with higher amounts of amorphous material in their molecular structure have both higher heats of wetting and greater extensibility, and that the conclusion by Ashpole that hydrogen bonds are largely responsible for the strength of the fibre right up to the breaking point is unwarranted. Further, the fact that the point for Bengals cotton falls well on the curve presented by Ashpole relating heat of wetting and work of rupture is no less surprising than the fact that the point for Sea Island cotton falls well off this curve, for it would be expected that the difference in the fine structure of cotton and of regenerated cellulose would preclude any good correlation between heat of wetting and work of rupture.

THERMODYNAMICS OF ABSORPTION

It is interesting from the theoretical viewpoint to compare the heat and the free energy of absorption of moisture by textile materials.

In this connection, the Gibbs–Helmholtz equation may be applied, relating the changes in the total (or internal) energy, in the work content (or free energy) and in the unavailable energy (or entropy) of the system.

For the absorption process, we have the Gibbs–Helmholtz equation:

$$\Delta G = Q_L - T.\Delta S \qquad \ldots.(11)$$

i.e.,

$$\Delta S = \frac{Q_L - \Delta G}{T} \qquad \ldots.(12)$$

where ΔG is the decrease in free energy, Q_L is the heat of absorption lost by the system, and ΔS is the decrease in entropy, when 1 gram of liquid water is absorbed by an infinite quantity of the textile material possessing a moisture regain α at the absolute temperature T.

The decrease in free energy per gram of liquid water absorbed is given by

$$\Delta G = \frac{RT}{M} \log_e \frac{p_s}{p} \qquad \ldots.(13)$$

where p is the equilibrium water-vapour pressure of the partially saturated cellulose of regain α at the absolute temperature T, p_s the saturation vapour pressure at that temperature, R the gas constant and M the molecular weight of water. p/p_s is thus the relative humidity at the temperature T with which the cellulose–water system is in equilibrium.

In *Figure 28*, the free energy, calculated from equation (13), and the differential heat of absorption of liquid water are plotted against relative humidity, the latter being derived from the combined results of Rees (*3*) and Guthrie (*4*) for eighteen types of cellulosic fibres. It is apparent that the decrease in heat content (Q_L) of the cellulose–water system is greater than the decrease in free energy (ΔG), and this shows, by reference to equation (12), that the absorption of water by cellulose is accompanied by a decrease in the entropy, or unavailable energy, of the system. The difference between the heat and the free-energy terms represents an excess energy which shows by how much the energy of binding of the water molecule to the cellulose surface exceeds the energy of attraction between a water molecule and a free water surface. This excess energy, calculated from the curves of *Figure 28*, is shown graphically in *Figure 29*. The curve relating entropy decrease and relative humidity is identical in shape to the excess energy curve, since, by equation (12), ΔS = excess energy/T. The values of the decrease in entropy are shown on the right-hand ordinate of *Figure 29*.

The following deductions may be made from *Figure 29*:

(1) The excess energy is greatest at the lower values of relative humidity; therefore, water molecules are most strongly attracted at low vapour pressures. The first molecules are

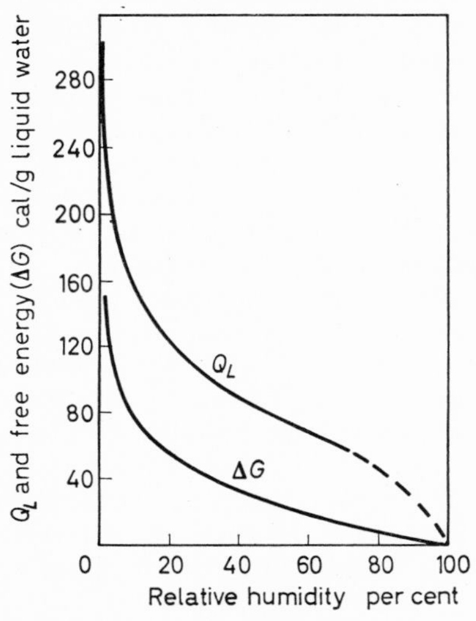

Figure 28. Relation of differential heat of absorption of liquid water and free energy to relative humidity

absorbed on sites where the attractive force is greatest and, as more molecules are attracted, the attractive force decreases, due to the water molecules exerting a repulsive force

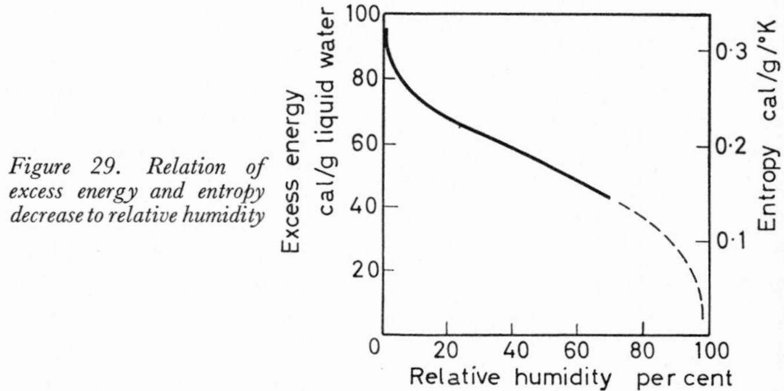

Figure 29. Relation of excess energy and entropy decrease to relative humidity

on one another, or to the formation of multi-layers of molecules.

(2) The water initially absorbed at a low relative humidity has an excess energy of 80–90 cal/g, which is roughly equal to

the latent heat of fusion of ice, indicating that the first water molecules absorbed have degrees of orientation and association comparable to that of ice.

(3) The curve flattens out at intermediate values of relative humidity with a rapid drop above a relative humidity of 80% due to the change to capillary condensation corresponding to the steep part of the absorption isotherm. The flat portion of the curve indicates that, but for capillary absorption, there would be an energy excess of absorbed over free water even up to saturation.

As long as absorption is molecular rather than capillary, it may be assumed that there is an entropy difference between the absorbed and the liquid states.

(4) Even near saturation, there appears to be a finite excess energy of absorbed over free water. Wahba (*14*) suggests that this indicates that the absorbed liquid near saturation may still be different from bulk liquid, possibly due to some change in the properties of the liquid when present in fine capillaries.

(5) The decrease in entropy is greatest at low values of relative humidity. The results of Rees and Guthrie yield a value of 0·29 cal/g/°K near dryness, which is in good agreement with the value of 0·28 obtained by Babbitt (*13*) from data on cotton and wood cellulose.

Absorption at very low relative humidities

Figure 28 (p. 52) shows that Q_L is greater than ΔG over a wide range of relative humidity. However, equation (13) shows that, as p/p_s tends to zero, ΔG tends to infinity; therefore, if the absorption process is accompanied by a decrease in entropy over the entire relative humidity range, Q_L should also tend to infinity as the relative humidity tends to zero. There is, however, no experimental evidence of this: on the contrary, all the evidence points to a finite value of Q_L at zero regain of about 290 cal/g. In particular, the experiments of Neale and Stringfellow (*20*), which were carried out at very low moisture regains, yielded a value of 289 cal/g for cotton cellulose at a moisture regain of 0·012%, corresponding to a relative humidity of 0·006%. The free energy at this relative humidity is about 320 cal/g at 25°C, which exceeds the Q_L value, indicating an increase in entropy. Babbitt (*13*) is unwilling to assume that the experimental determinations of Q_L are in error near dryness, and thus doubts the validity of the thermodynamical equation (11) in this region, but has applied it at higher humidities.

In *Figure 30* the differential heat and the free-energy curves of *Figure 28* have been plotted on a much extended scale of relative humidity, the curves being limited to the very low relative humidity values from zero to 1%. The corresponding curve for entropy change is also shown. These curves, derived from the experimental results of Rees (*3*) and Guthrie (*4*), show that at a certain very low relative humidity, viz., 0·014%, the entropy change is zero, from which it would appear that the absorbed water at this humidity is similar to free water. The corresponding moisture regain for cotton cellulose

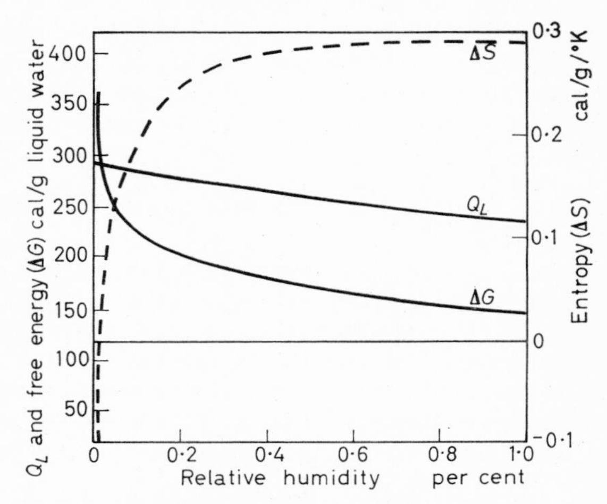

Figure 30. Relation of differential heat of absorption, free energy and entropy change to relative humidity

is 0·027%. For all values of moisture regain greater than 0·027%, the absorption of water by cotton cellulose would therefore be accompanied by a *decrease* in entropy right up to saturation, but below this value of regain, it would be accompanied by an *increase* in entropy. This would seem to indicate that, for moisture regains below about 0·03% for cotton cellulose, the water molecules in the absorbed phase are more at random than in the bulk liquid, although they lie under the effect of the attractive forces of the absorbent surface. Wahba (*14*) sees no reason to suppose that the entropy change accompanying absorption should always be negative at the early stages, and puts forward the following theory.

When water is absorbed by the textile material, the three-dimensional motion of the water molecules in the bulk liquid is changed to a two-dimensional motion in the absorbed film, and this greater degree of organization in the absorbed phase means that there is a *decrease* in entropy. However, the separation of the liquid molecules from each other in spreading on the absorbent surface causes an *increase* in entropy, as in the spontaneous expansion of a gas, and these two effects may balance out at a low concentration of water on the surface. As the absorbed molecules crowd on the surface of the absorbent, the former effect (increased orderliness) exceeds the latter effect (expansion), resulting in a net decrease in entropy, which will increase in magnitude as the concentration of water molecules in the absorbed film increases. However, as the film thickens by the absorption of water molecules in successive layers, the forces holding the outer molecules will weaken, so that they are more randomized, and there will be a continuous diminution of the entropy decrease up to saturation, as shown in *Figure 29* (p. 52).

SIGNIFICANCE OF THE THERMAL DATA IN RELATION TO THE BINDING OF WATER TO CELLULOSE

The large magnitude of the differential heat of absorption, and the large entropy decrease near dryness, indicate that the initial reaction of water with cellulose is similar to the formation of primary chemical bonds. Hydrogen bonding undoubtedly plays an essential role in the absorption of moisture by textiles—the water molecules interact with the hydroxyl groups of the cellulose, and there is a replacement of hydrogen bonds between cellulose molecules by bonds between water and cellulose molecules.

The differential heat of absorption of water vapour by dry cellulose has been shown to be 15·7 kcal/mol, or of liquid water 5·2 kcal/mol (i.e., 290 cal/g of liquid water). Now, the energy of formation of a hydrogen bond is about 5 kcal/mol, and this is roughly the value obtained for Q_L at zero moisture regain. However, this heat of absorption is the difference between the heat of formation of the bonds formed between the cellulose and the water molecules and the heat of formation of the bonds between the cellulose molecules that are broken. Therefore, if hydrogen bonding is to be the cause of the heat of absorption, twice as many bonds must be formed as are broken.

Neale and Stringfellow (*20*) suggest that there are unsaturated hydroxyl groups in the amorphous regions of the cellulose structure, and that, in the primary absorption stage, each water molecule is directly linked to a pair of suitably placed hydroxyl groups by strong hydrogen bonds, the extra hydrogen bond accounting for the large heat change.

THERMOSTATIC ACTION OF HYGROSCOPIC TEXTILE MATERIALS WHEN USED FOR CLOTHING

The primary function of clothing in the temperate and cold latitudes is to decrease the heat loss from the body to its surroundings. The human body can adjust its thermal conductivity to cope with small changes in environment, but only slowly, so that if there is a sudden drop in temperature the adjustment made by the body is temporarily too small and a sensation of chill is felt. Clothing will help in avoiding this effect if it delays the change of temperature at the skin.

The water-vapour content of the atmosphere is roughly the same in a well-ventilated room as it is outdoors, and the change in conditions in winter time from indoors to outdoors is a decrease in temperature accompanied by an increase in relative humidity. Consider a mass of textile fibres being moved from a warm room to the colder atmosphere outdoors. The fibres will lose heat by virtue of their thermal capacity (the specific heat effect), but, due to the increase in relative humidity, moisture will be absorbed by the fibres and, consequently, heat of absorption will be liberated, which will check the rate of cooling of the mass, thereby delaying the change of temperature at the skin. Cassie (*21*, *22*) has shown that, for atmospheric changes of this nature, the change in temperature is propagated through the fibres with two components, one a fast one due to the specific heat of the fibres, and the other a much slower one due to the hygroscopic property of the fibres with its accompanied evolution of heat.

The magnitude of the heat evolved in such a change of atmospheric conditions may be calculated by the equation:

$$q = m(\alpha_2 - \alpha_1)\,Q_v \qquad \ldots.(14)$$

where m is the mass of the dry textile material, α_2 and α_1 are the equilibrium fractional moisture regains of the material for outdoor and indoor conditions, respectively, Q_v is the differential heat of absorption of water vapour by the material at the regain α_1, and q is the total heat liberated. For example, in passing from a room at 20°C and 40% relative humidity to the outside air at 10°C and 90% relative humidity, a wool garment weighing one kilogram will liberate about 83 kilocalories, which is almost as much as the body produces by its metabolism in one hour. A kilogram of cotton undergoing the same atmospheric changes will liberate about 50 kilocalories, and a kilogram of viscose rayon about 88 kilocalories.

The thermostatic action of wool fibres in delaying the propagation of a temperature change through the fibre mass is illustrated in *Figure 31*, which shows the results of an experiment by Cassie (*21*) in which air with a constant water-vapour pressure was forced through a cylindrical plug of the fibres. Air at 15°C was forced through the wool until it was fully conditioned, and then the temperature of the air was raised to 31°C. Curve A shows the temperature change for the air stream, which would be similar for a mass of fibres having zero specific heat and no hygroscopic property. Curve C shows the temperature change for a mass of fibres having positive specific heat but no hygroscopic property. Curve B shows the temperature change for a mass of fibres having positive specific heat and hygroscopicity.

The temperature change in the surrounding air begins to be propagated through the fibres as if they had no hygroscopic property, but is quickly halted at a temperature approximately half-way to the

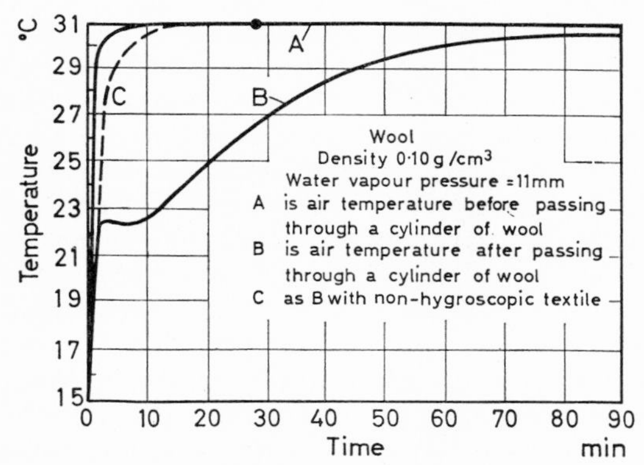

Figure 31. Thermostatic effect of hygroscopic textiles

(By courtesy of *J. Text. Inst.*, 1940)

final one, due to the effect of the heat of absorption liberated. Thereafter, the temperature of the mass rises slowly to 31°C.

Cassie (*21*) has shown that, if t_s is the time required for the temperature to reach a given value due to the specific heat effect, and t_H is the time to reach the same temperature due to the hygroscopic effect, then

$$t_H/t_s = A.\sigma \qquad \ldots.(15)$$

where A is a factor involving the specific heat of the textile material and the specific heat and density of the air, and σ is one of the proportionality constants in the following expression, due to Henry (*23*), relating moisture regain α, water vapour concentration C and temperature T:

$$\frac{\partial \alpha}{\partial t} = \sigma \frac{\partial C}{\partial t} - \omega \frac{\partial T}{\partial t} \qquad \ldots.(16)$$

For wool, equation (15) yields a value of about 20:1 for the ratio t_H/t_s, so that the time required to establish a temperature change in wool is roughly twenty times that which would be required if the fibres were non-hygroscopic. In *Figure 31*, the time required to reach, say, 27°C, by following curves B and C, is roughly 20:1.

Cassie's experiment illustrates the thermostatic effect of the textile against an increase in temperature, but a similar effect would be observed against a decrease in temperature.

One notes from equation (15) that the ratio of the two times increases as σ increases. Equation (16) shows that σ is proportional to the rate of increase of moisture regain with relative humidity, so that the steeper the absorption isotherm, the more difficult it is to change the temperature of the textile.

A similar experiment to that illustrated in *Figure 31* using cotton in place of wool fibres would show roughly the same initial rapid rise of temperature to a value approximately half-way to the final temperature, but a greater rate of increase thereafter to the final temperature than for the wool. The cotton, however, would also produce a marked thermostatic effect compared with a non-hygroscopic material.

REFERENCES

1 G. H. Argue and O. Maass, *Canad. J. Res.*, **12,** 564 (1935).
2 H. B. Dunford and J. L. Morrison, *Canad. J. Chem.*, **33,** 904 (1955).
3 W. H. Rees, *J. Text. Inst.*, **39,** T351 (1948).
4 J. C. Guthrie, *J. Text. Inst.*, **40,** T489 (1949).
5 M. Wahba, *J. Phys. & Colloid Chem.*, **52,** 1197 (1948).
6 P. T. Newsome and S. E. Sheppard, *J. Phys. Chem.*, **36,** 930 (1932).
7 S. A. Shorter, *J. Text. Inst.*, **15,** T328 (1924).
8 A. R. Urquhart and A. M. Williams, *J. Text. Inst.*, **15,** T559 (1924).
9 M. Wahba and S. Nashed, *Nature*, **166,** 998 (1950).
10 J. J. Hedges, *Trans. Faraday Soc.*, **22,** 178 (1926).
11 W. H. Rees, unpublished.
12 J. B. Speakman and A. K. Saville, *J. Text. Inst.*, **37,** P271 (1946).
13 J. D. Babbitt, *Canad. J. Res.*, **20A,** 143 (1942).
14 M. Wahba, *J. Phys. Chem.*, **54,** 1148 (1950).
15 J. B. Taylor, *J. Text. Inst.*, **43,** T489 (1952).
16 J. B. Taylor, *J. Text. Inst.*, **45,** T642 (1954).
17 E. K. Strachan, *Amer. Dyest. Rep.*, **27,** 240 (1938).
18 D. K. Ashpole, *Nature*, **169,** 37 (1952).
19 R. Meredith, *J. Text. Inst.*, **36,** T107 (1945).
20 S. M. Neale and W. A. Stringfellow, *Trans. Faraday Soc.*, **37,** 525 (1941).
21 A. B. D. Cassie, *J. Text. Inst.*, **31,** T17 (1940).
22 A. B. D. Cassie *et al.*, *Trans. Faraday Soc.*, **36,** 445, 453, 458 (1940).
23 P. S. H. Henry, *Proc. Roy. Soc.*, **171A,** 215 (1939).

CHAPTER 5

TWO- OR THREE-PHASE ADSORPTION THEORIES

By G. King

There are several theories that attempt to explain the adsorption* of moisture by textile materials. This is due partly to our lack of knowledge concerning the sorption process, but also to the absence of any critical test that may be applied to each theory. It is relatively easy to develop a sorption isotherm to fit the experimental relation with the aid of two or three adjustable coefficients, but this is not a sufficiently exacting criterion on which to judge the theory. We can only ensure that the theory does not violate accepted physical principles.

The theories fall roughly into two groups. Peirce (*1*), and Brunauer, Emmett and Teller (*2*), for example, consider the water molecules to be adsorbed* on internal surfaces or sites in the adsorbent, and apart from supplying these sites the textile is considered to play little part in the process. On the other hand, Katz (*3*), and Hailwood and Horrobin (*4*), consider the process to be one of solution. It is probable that both these lines of approach are partly correct, the former at low water concentrations, and the latter as we approach saturation.

PEIRCE'S THEORY

It is about twenty-eight years since Peirce developed the first adsorption isotherm for textiles in order to explain the effect of adsorbed water on the elastic properties of cotton. He made a most important contribution to the theory when he postulated two possible forms of adsorbed water, one chemically bound to the cotton, and the remainder adsorbed in liquid form. This concept has been employed by all succeeding investigators in the field.

While examining the effect of regain on the rigidity modulus of a cotton hair, Peirce found that the rigidity decreased exponentially as the regain increased, i.e., the logarithm of the rigidity modulus varied inversely as the regain (*Figure 32*). In order to explain this effect he assumed that only part of the adsorbed water was influencing

* The word adsorption is used to denote the attachment of water to specific sites as distinct from the random mixing of molecules which occurs in solution.

the modulus and that this part was adsorbed first and was chemically bound to the cotton. The remaining fraction was assumed to be adsorbed with little or no effect. Peirce then determined the relative concentrations of the two types of adsorbed water, by considering the chance of a water molecule from the surrounding vapour coming into contact with either a reactive or a non-reactive group in the cellulose molecule.

If we name the reactive and inactive sites α and β, respectively, then the affinity of the α sites is considered to be so much greater than that of the β sites that no β site will be occupied until all the adjacent

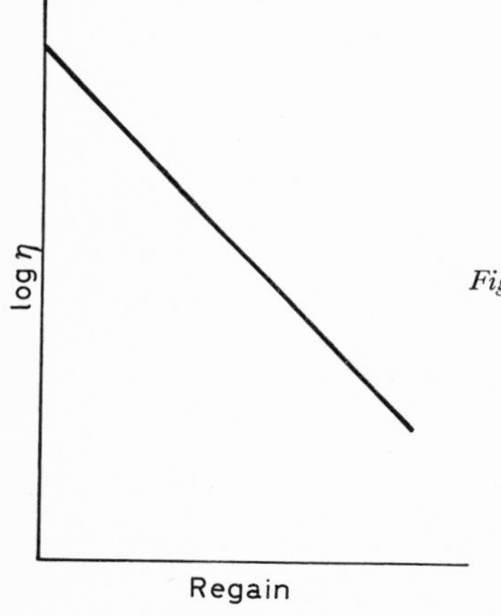

Figure 32. Relation between rigidity modulus and moisture regain

α sites are filled. This assumption may be further simplified by considering the water occupying the β sites to be associated with that occupying α sites. Although Peirce does not state that the 'β' water covers the 'α' water, he does suggest that the presence of 'β' water prevents evaporation of the 'α' water, which is almost the same thing, and it leads to a simpler picture of the process.

Peirce's theory is then developed as follows. If, at any stage in the adsorption, there are C moles of water adsorbed per mole of repeat molecular groups in the cellulose chain, then

$$C = C_\alpha + C_\beta$$

where C_α is the molar concentration of the bound, or 'α', water

C_β is the molar concentration of the liquid, or 'β', water.

Therefore, C_α moles of hexose groups will be occupied and $(1-C_\alpha)$ will be free. Now, if C increases by a small amount dC, the fraction

(dC_α) which falls on the unoccupied groups will be proportional to ($1-C_\alpha$).

Therefore, $$dC_\alpha = g(1-C_\alpha).dC$$
where g is a constant, or

$$C_\alpha = 1-e^{-gC} \quad \text{and} \quad C_\beta = C-1+e^{-gC}$$

Then, if it is assumed that the change in rigidity of the fibre arises from the presence of the bound 'α' molecules, with the proviso that each molecule is equally effective, a linear relation between C_α and rigidity must lead to a logarithmic relation between moisture regain and rigidity (η), i.e.,

$$\eta \propto C_\alpha \quad \text{or} \quad \eta \propto (1-e^{-gC})$$

Equilibrium with the external water vapour

In order to determine the adsorption isotherm it is now necessary to determine the equilibrium relation between the adsorbed water

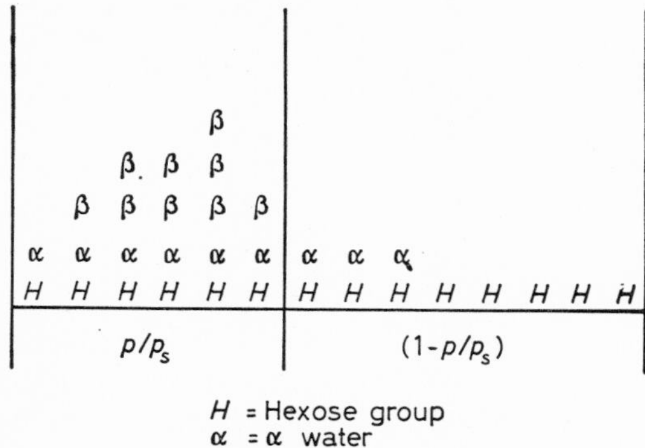

Figure 33. Evaporating and non-evaporating areas of cotton fibre surface

and the external vapour pressure. Peirce assumed that it was largely the liquid or 'β' water that contributed to the vapour pressure. If p is the vapour pressure for a total adsorption and p_s is the saturation pressure, Peirce assumes that the effective evaporating area will be proportional to p/p_s. This is not necessarily proportional to C_β, because he considers that more than one layer of 'β' molecules may be present, and only exposed layers contribute to the evaporation. We have then an effective evaporating area p/p_s and a non-evaporating area $(1-p/p_s)$, as shown in *Figure 33*.

If p increases by a small amount $\mathrm{d}p$ and C_β by $\mathrm{d}C_\beta$, the increase in evaporation will come only from the fraction of $\mathrm{d}C_\beta$ which falls on that part of the absorbing surface not already covered by 'β' molecules. The non-evaporating fraction is $(1-p/p_s)$, and so the increase in evaporation will be proportional to $(1-p/p_s).\mathrm{d}C_\beta$. We may then write

$$(1-p/p_s).\mathrm{d}C_\beta = S.\mathrm{d}p/p_s$$

where S is a constant. Integration of this expression leads to

$$p/p_s = 1-\mathrm{e}^{-C_\beta/S}$$

Contribution of bound molecules

Peirce introduces a correction to allow for some evaporation from the 'α' molecules. He assumes that only those uncovered by the β molecules can evaporate. They will be contained in the fraction $(1-p/p_s) = \mathrm{e}^{-C_\beta/S}$ of the evaporating surface, which in turn will contain $C_\alpha.\mathrm{e}^{-C_\beta/S}$ bound molecules. The effective evaporating area, p/p_s, must therefore be increased by an amount proportional to this quantity, giving

$$p/p_s = 1-\mathrm{e}^{-C_\beta/S}+KC_\alpha\,\mathrm{e}^{-C_\beta/S}$$

where K is a constant.

If values of C_α and C_β in terms of C, as derived above, are substituted in this equation, it becomes a relation between regain and relative humidity which can be fitted to experimental data.

Heat of sorption of α molecules

At low water concentrations, when C_β is very small, the isotherm relation reduces to

$$p/p_s = K.C_\alpha = KgC$$
$$\approx KC \; (g \approx 1)$$

K may then be considered to be the equilibrium constant for the chemical combination of the water vapour with the cellulose. We can then apply the well-known thermodynamic relation

$$R.\frac{\partial \log_e K}{\partial T} = H/T^2 \quad \text{or} \quad \log_e K = A-H/RT$$

where H is the molar heat of adsorption, R is the gas constant, T is the absolute temperature, and A is a constant.

Then, if K is determined from a series of isotherms at different temperatures, the slope of the graph of $\log_e K$ against $1/T$ gives H/R.

The value of H found by Peirce was about 14·7 kcal/mole. If we allow about 10 kcal/mole for the molar latent heat of condensation of water, the heat of adsorption from liquid water is about 4·7 kcal/mole.

Criticism of the theory

This theory has been criticized by Gilbert (*5*) on the grounds that there is no microscopic balancing of the evaporation and condensation processes, in accordance with the theories of Langmuir (*6*) and Brunauer, Emmett and Teller (*2*).

A second criticism of Gilbert's is not, however, valid. This

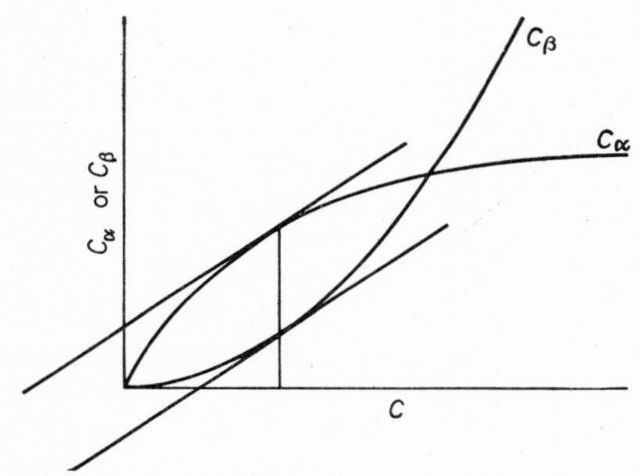

Figure 34. Relation of water concentration on α- and β-sites to total adsorbed water concentration

concerns the relative affinity of the 'α' and 'β' molecules for their respective sites in the cellulose. From the relation already mentioned, namely, $dC_\alpha = g(1 - C_\alpha)\,dC$, and for $g = 1$, $C_\alpha = \frac{1}{2}$; therefore

$$dC_\alpha = \tfrac{1}{2}dC = dC_\beta$$

Gilbert states that this situation is impossible, for at this stage dC is equally distributed amongst both types of sites in spite of their different reactivities. This is not impossible, however, and is merely due to the fact that the number of sites for the 'β' water increases with increased absorption, whereas the number of α sites decreases. The absorption of 'β' water therefore increases rapidly, while C_α approaches a saturation value (*Figure 34*). At some stage the slopes of the two relations must be equal. Similar conclusions also apply to the Brunauer, Emmett and Teller isotherm.

Peirce's derivation is not clear at all points, but it has supplied many ideas for later workers, and as such its value cannot be overestimated.

Application to wool

Speakman (*7*) has analysed the water adsorbed by wool into three fractions. Applying Peirce's relation, $p/p_s = (1 - e^{-C_\beta/S})$, he first obtained an estimate of the 'α' and 'β' water present. He then examined the resulting relation between C_α and the relative rigidity of wool at corresponding regains. However, unlike the similar relation for cotton, this was not a simple linear expression, which

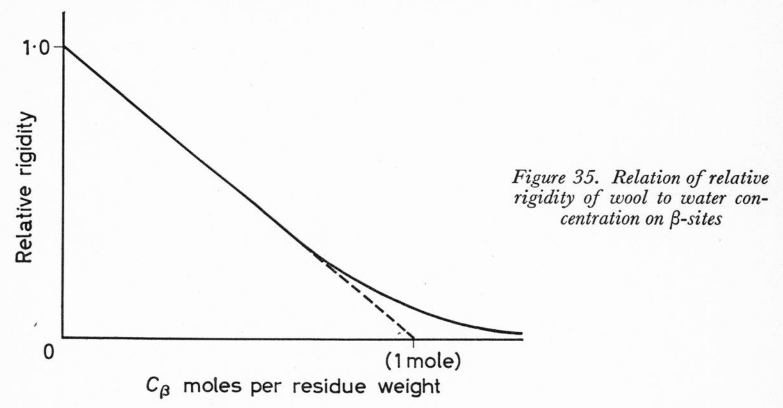

Figure 35. Relation of relative rigidity of wool to water concentration on β-sites

implied that there was no direct relationship between the 'α' water and the rigidity of wool.

Speakman did, however, find a linear relationship between the concentration of 'β' water and the rigidity, over the range 0–80% relative humidity. A slight deviation from linearity above 80% r.h. was attributed to capillary water, which was considered to have no effect on the elastic properties of the wool (*Figure 35*). Extrapolation of the linear portion of the curve gives the amount of 'β' water required to complete the reduction in rigidity, and this amounts to one mole of water per mole of repeat units in the polypeptide chain. We have then a simple mechanism for the reduction in rigidity, if each 'β' water molecule breaks a hydrogen bond joining the main polypeptide chains and thus loosens the structure.

Now, as a result of earlier experiments, Speakman had obtained a relation between the relative humidity and the reduction in relative rigidity of the wool fibre

$$\Delta\eta = \nu h^\lambda$$

where $\Delta\eta$ is the reduction in relative rigidity, h is the relative humidity, and ν and λ are constants.

But, we have a 'one-to-one' relation between the molar concentration of the 'β' water and $\Delta\eta$ (*Figure 35*); therefore, $C_\beta = \nu h^\lambda$. The original relation due to Peirce may then be replaced by this experimentally derived relation, and for any value of h it is possible to subdivide the adsorbed water into three fractions: C_α, C_β, and capillary water.

Speakman goes on to suggest that the 'β' water is adsorbed without evolution of heat, because hydrogen bonds are broken in the process. He therefore associates the heat of adsorption with the 'α' water which is considered to combine with reactive side chains, and then

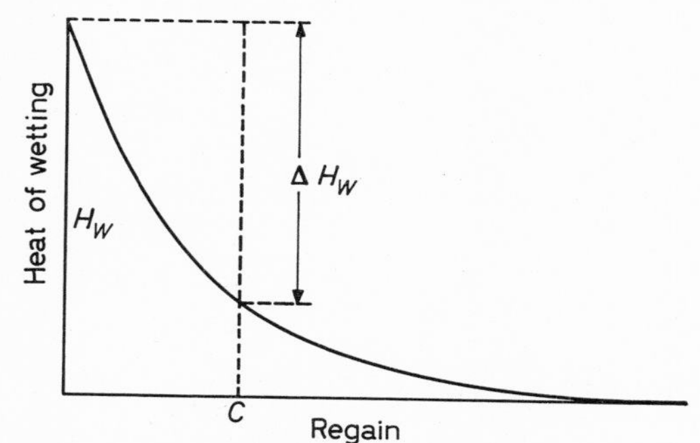

Figure 36. Heat of wetting and moisture regain for wool

determines the molar heat of adsorption from the data for heat of wetting given by Hedges (*8*).

From Hedges's relation we can obtain the heat evolved, ΔH_w, for a given increase in water concentration from zero to C (*Figure 36*). This amount of heat was shown to be proportional to C_α over a wide range. The heat of adsorption per mole of 'α' water turns out to be 5·8 kcal, which is close to the heat of hydration of the available side-chain groups.

HAILWOOD AND HORROBIN'S THEORY

Hailwood and Horrobin (*4*) have developed a sorption isotherm by analogy with simple solution theory. They consider that the absorbed water exists partly in chemical combination with the polymer, as water of hydration, and partly in solid solution. Furthermore, the three species, namely polymer, dissolved water and polymer hydrate, are considered to form an ideal solution.

In their derivation the authors consider the general case with many degrees of hydration, but for simplicity it is proposed to take the case where the monohydrate only is formed; the principles involved are not affected by this modification. Then, if

a_H is the chemical activity of the hydrate in the solid solution,

a_P is that of the unhydrated polymer, and

a_W is that of the dissolved water,

then, for equilibrium between these three species,

$$a_H = a_P . a_W . K_1$$

where K_1 is the corresponding equilibrium constant.

Similarly, for equilibrium between the dissolved water and the water vapour,

$$a_W = K_2 . h/100$$

where K_2 is the equilibrium constant and h the external relative humidity.

But, if the solid solution is considered to be ideal, the activities of the species may be replaced by their mole fractions, and if there are x moles of hydrated polymer, y moles of dissolved water and x_0 moles of unhydrated polymer present, then

$$a_H = x/(y+x+x_0)$$
$$a_W = y/(y+x+x_0)$$
$$a_P = x_0/(y+x+x_0)$$

and, substituting for a_H and a_P, we have

$$x = x_0 . a_W . K_1 = x_0 K_1 K_2 h/100$$

and $$y/(y+x+x_0) = K_2 h/100$$

Therefore, $$y/(x+x_0) = K_2 h/(100-K_2 h)$$

But, the total amount of water in the solid phase is $(x+y)$ moles, and the total amount of polymer (hydrated or unhydrated) is $(x+x_0)$ moles. Therefore, the total molar concentration of absorbed water in the polymer is

$$C = \frac{y+x}{x+x_0} = \frac{y}{x+x_0} + \frac{x}{x+x_0}$$

i.e., $$C = \frac{Mr}{1800} = \frac{K_2 h}{100-K_2 h} + \frac{K_1 K_2 h}{100+K_1 K_2 h}$$

where r is the regain and M the molecular weight of the polymer.

The authors fitted the above relation to a series of experimental isotherms for different textile materials, assuming suitable values of K_1, K_2 and M. They found that the value of M required for a reasonable fit was always greater than the molecular weight of the repeat polar group in the polymer chain (Z). Hailwood and Horrobin resolved this difficulty by allowing for the presence in the polymer of crystalline material which was considered to be inaccessible to the adsorbed water. They then derived a relation $\frac{M-Z}{M}$ as giving an estimate of the fraction of the polymer which existed in a highly crystalline state.

Employing standard thermodynamic relations, the heat of hydration and the heat of solution of water in the polymer may be obtained. For the two equilibrium relations with constants K_1 and K_2, we have

$$R\cdot\frac{\partial}{\partial T}\cdot\log_e K_1 = \Delta H_1/T^2$$

and

$$R\cdot\frac{\partial}{\partial T}\cdot\log_e K_2 = \Delta H_2/T^2$$

where ΔH_1 is the heat of hydration from water in the adsorbed state per mole of hydrate and ΔH_2 is the heat of adsorption of the water in the solid solution. Then, if a molar concentration C of total adsorbed water is made up of C_1 moles of dissolved water and C_2 moles of water of hydration, the total heat exchange will be $C_1\Delta H_2+C_2(\Delta H_1+\Delta H_2)$, and, similarly, the heat of wetting H_W is

$$H_W = (C_{1_{\text{sat.}}}-C_1)\,\Delta H_2+(C_{2_{\text{sat.}}}-C_2)\,(\Delta H_2+\Delta H_1).$$

The authors state that the agreement between this heat of wetting relation and Hedges's experimental data for wool is fairly good, but do not publish comparative results. They suggest that Hedges's data may be inaccurate at low regains, where the discrepancy is greatest.

In further support of their adsorption theory, they calculated the specific volume of the solid solution of polymer, hydrate, and dissolved water for different regains. As this is an ideal solution and there is no volume change on mixing, the volume of the solid solution will be given by $(yv_1+xv_2+x_0v_3)$, where v_1 is the molar volume of the dissolved water, v_2 is that of the hydrate, and v_3 that of the free polymer. The specific volume of the phase, v, is then given by

$$v = \frac{yv_1+xv_2+x_0v_3}{x(M+18)+x_0M+18y} = \frac{C_1v_1+C_2v_2+C_3v_3}{M+18(C_1+C_2)}$$

where $C_1 = \frac{y}{x+x_0}$; $C_2 = \frac{x}{x+x_0}$; $C_3 = \frac{x_0}{x+x_0}$.

The relation between v and the regain was fitted to King's (*9*) swelling data for wool (*Figure 37*).

In spite of the good description of experimental data obtained with this model, it has been criticized by Gee and Barrer (4). The main criticism is that the solid solution cannot be considered as ideal, especially when species of totally different molecular size are included. Solutions of long-chain polymers are known to differ considerably from ideal solutions. Cassie (4) has questioned the doubt

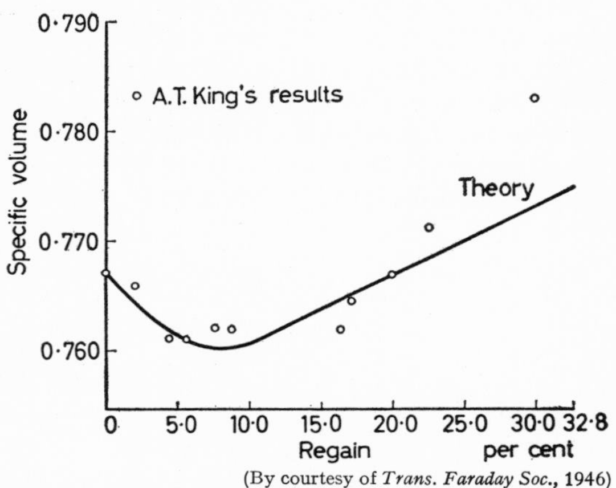

(By courtesy of *Trans. Faraday Soc.*, 1946)

Figure 37. Specific volume and moisture regain for wool

cast on Hedges's experimental data for heat of wetting, which he considers may be the most reproducible data available for the keratin–water system.

REFERENCES

1 F. T. Peirce, *J. Text. Inst.*, **20,** T133 (1929).
2 S. Brunauer, P. H. Emmett and F. Teller, *J. Amer. Chem. Soc.*, **60,** 309 (1938).
3 J. R. Katz, *Kolloid Beih.*, **9,** 1 (1917–18); *Trans. Faraday Soc.*, **29,** 279 (1933).
4 A. J. Hailwood and S. Horrobin, General Discussion on Swelling and Shrinking, *Trans. Faraday Soc.*, **42B**, 84 (1946).
5 G. A. Gilbert, *J. Soc. Dyers Col.*, Symposium 'Fibrous Proteins', 96 (1946).
6 I. Langmuir, *J. Amer. Chem. Soc.*, **40,** 1361 (1918).
7 J. B. Speakman, *Trans. Faraday Soc.*, **40,** 6 (1944).
8 J. J. Hedges, *Trans. Faraday Soc.*, **22,** 178 (1926).
9 A. T. King, *J. Text. Inst.*, **17,** T61 (1926).

CHAPTER 6

THEORIES OF MULTI-LAYER ADSORPTION

By G. King

As long ago as 1918 Langmuir (*1*) developed a simple theory of sorption limited to the formation of unimolecular layers on solid surfaces. He did this simply by equating the rate of evaporation of gas molecules from the surface with the rate of condensation from the surrounding gas or vapour. Very simply then, the rate of evaporation will be proportional to the surface covered by adsorbed molecules

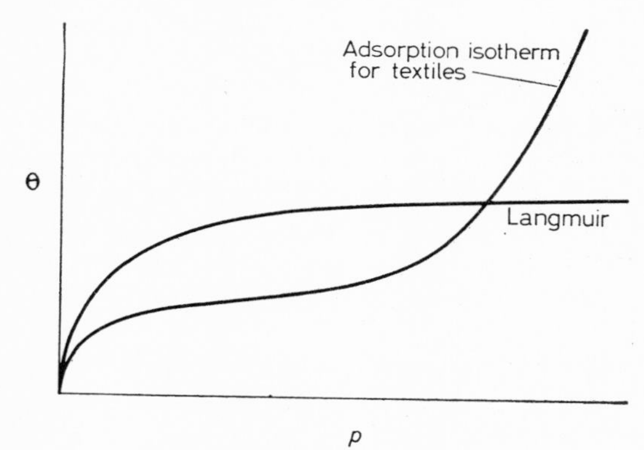

Figure 38. Adsorption isotherms

(A_a). The rate of condensation will be proportional to the uncovered surface (A_0) and to the vapour pressure (p). Therefore,

$$k_a . A_a = k_0 . p . A_0 \qquad \ldots . (1)$$

And, if the total surface area is $A = (A_a + A_0)$, then

$$p = k . A_0/(A - A_a) = k . \theta/(1 - \theta) \qquad \ldots . (2)$$

where θ is the fractional adsorption for a pressure p. This relation gives the well-known isotherm which describes only some adsorption processes, the more general shape being more like the normal textile regain curves with a point of inflexion (*Figure 38*).

One is, therefore, led to consider adsorption in amounts greater than the monolayer. Langmuir did extend his theory in this way, but did not derive an isotherm. Many years later, however, Brunauer, Emmett and Teller (*2*) developed a multilayer adsorption mechanism similar to that of Langmuir and extended it to derive a multimolecular adsorption isotherm. The method is simply to extend the evaporation–condensation mechanism to many layers of adsorbed molecules.

Consider a surface covered by groups of molecules; there will be free surface together with groups containing 1, 2, 3, etc. layers of molecules. Let A_0 be the area of uncovered surface, A_1 the area covered by one layer of molecules, and A_i be the area covered by i layers of molecules; i.e., the molecules can be arranged as shown in *Figure 39*.

Figure 39. Multi-layer adsorption on solid surfaces

For equilibrium we may equate the rates of evaporation and condensation from each successive layer, and for the first layer we have

$$a_1 p A_0 = k_1 A_1 \qquad \ldots.(3)$$

and the general expression is

$$a_i p A_{i-1} = k_i A_i \qquad \ldots.(4)$$

The k coefficients include a term which governs the rate of evaporation of the adsorbed molecules. These can leave the surface only if they acquire an energy equal to the energy of binding to the surface. The fraction of molecules acquiring the necessary evaporation energy at any instant will be given by Boltzmann's expression $e^{-U_i/RT}$, where U_i is the binding energy for the ith layer, R is the gas constant, and T is the absolute temperature. Therefore, we can write

$$k_1 = b_1 e^{-U_i/RT} \qquad \ldots.(5)$$

and, in general,

$$k_i = b_i e^{-U_i/RT} \qquad \ldots.(6)$$

where b_1, b_2, etc. are constants.

The total surface area $= \sum_0^\infty A_i = A_0'$ (say), and the total volume adsorbed $= v = v_0 \sum_0^\infty i . A_i$ (the area A_i is covered with i layers), where v_0 is the volume of gas adsorbed per unit area of monolayer. Therefore,

$$\frac{v}{A_0'.v_0} = \frac{v}{v_m} = v_0 \sum_0^\infty i.A_i/v_0 \sum_0^\infty A_i \qquad \ldots.(7)$$

Brunauer, Emmett and Teller now make two assumptions: (1) that $U_2 = U_3 = \ldots = U_L$ (heat of liquefaction of gas), (2) that $b_2/a_2 = b_3/a_3 = \ldots = d$, i.e., they assume that the absorbed gas is in a liquid state from the second layer outwards, so that the evaporation–condensation mechanism is similar for all layers except the first. Thus, we can write $A_2 = xA_1$, or in general $A_i = xA_{i-1}$, where

$$x = \frac{p}{d}.e^{U_L/RT} \qquad \ldots.(8)$$

and for the first layer $A_1 = A_0C.x$, where

$$C = \frac{a_1 d}{b_1}.e^{(U_1-U_L)/RT} \qquad \ldots.(9)$$

$$\text{Therefore, } \frac{v}{v_m} = \frac{A_1(1+2x+3x^2+\ldots)}{A_0+A_1(1+x+x^2+\ldots)} = \frac{A_0.C.x[1/(1-x)^2]}{A_0[1+Cx/(1-x)]}$$

$$= \frac{Cx}{(1-x)(1-x+Cx)} \qquad \ldots.(10)$$

for unrestricted adsorption.

At saturation ($p = p_s$) $v \to \infty$. But $v \to \infty$ when $x = 1$ in the above expression for the isotherm, so, from equation (8),

$$1 = \frac{p_s}{d}.e^{U_L/RT} \qquad \ldots.(11)$$

For $v \neq \infty$, $x = p/p_s$, and

$$v = \frac{v_m C.p}{(p_s-p)\{1+(C-1)\,p/p_s\}} \qquad \ldots.(12)$$

If the adsorption is restricted to a finite number of molecular layers, a more complicated isotherm relation is obtained. However, for small values of p/p_s, if the maximum number of layers is not less than about 5, the relation approximates to the above simple form. If the maximum number of molecular layers is unity, we have the original Langmuir relation for monomolecular adsorption.

The above relation may be put in a linear form

$$\frac{p}{v(p_s-p)} = \frac{1}{v_m.C}+\frac{C-1}{v_m.C}(p/p_s) \qquad \ldots.(13)$$

and by plotting $\frac{p}{v(p_s - p)}$ against p/p_s, v_m and C may be determined from the slope and intercept. But, $v_m = A_0'.v_0$, where A_0' is the area available for adsorption. Therefore, if v_0 can be estimated, it is possible to determine A_0'. Now,

$$C = \frac{a_1}{b_1} \cdot \frac{b_2}{a_2} \cdot e^{(U_1 - U_L)/RT} \qquad \ldots . (9)$$

and the authors assume that $a_1 b_2 / b_1 a_2 \approx 1$. Therefore,

$$C = e^{(U_1 - U_L)/RT} \qquad \ldots . (14)$$

from which one may determine the heat of adsorption of the first layer. However, Cassie (*3*) has obtained an expression for C employing a thermodynamic treatment and gives reasons to suggest that $a_1 b_2 / a_2 b_1 > 1$, and as a result the values for the heat of adsorption obtained by Brunauer, Emmett and Teller may be too low.

The Brunauer, Emmett and Teller (B.E.T.) theory of sorption is generally accepted as giving a reasonably accurate account of the adsorption process. It does fit textile isotherms, except at high vapour pressures, and many modifications have been suggested to account for this discrepancy.

The theory has been discussed by Cassie (*4*) and Gilbert (*5*), largely with respect to the structure of the outer adsorbed layers. The authors allow only short-range forces sufficient to bind the first adsorbed layer; further layers are adsorbed at vapour pressures below saturation, by virtue of a condensation–evaporation equilibrium. At the same time, however, the authors consider that the adsorbed water over and above the monolayer has the properties of liquid water. These two considerations are incompatible, for, as Cassie has pointed out, no adsorption could take place on the external layers if they were identical with liquid water. There could be no resulting decrease in free energy on transferring water molecules from liquid water to the outer adsorbed layers. It is also apparent from inspection of the B.E.T. model that the outer layers of water molecules are distributed in a manner completely different from that in liquid water.

CASSIE'S MULTIMOLECULAR ADSORPTION THEORY

As mentioned above, adsorption of vapours on solids, over and above the monolayer, in the absence of long-range forces binding these outer layers to the surface, has received justification only on thermodynamic grounds; Brunauer, Emmett and Teller argue that there are no such long-range forces present. According to the laws of thermodynamics, adsorption will take place only if the adsorbate suffers a reduction in free energy on being transferred from an external liquid to the adsorbed state.

The change in free energy at constant pressure is

$$\Delta G = \Delta H - T.\Delta S \quad \ldots.(15)$$

where ΔH is the heat exchange per mole, ΔS is the entropy exchange per mole, and T is the absolute temperature.

For a reduction in free energy, ΔG must be negative, and even if ΔS is zero or negative, i.e., the adsorbed molecules are in a more ordered state than in the liquid, then, provided that ΔH is negative (i.e., heat is evolved in the adsorption process), adsorption can still take place. However, if the heat evolved is from water adsorbed in the first layer only, then, for subsequent layers where $\Delta H = 0$, in order that ΔG be negative, ΔS must be positive. In other words, adsorption must then take place because the adsorbed molecules are in a more random state than in liquid water, i.e., by some mixing or distributive process analagous to the B.E.T. evaporation–condensation mechanism.

Cassie first developed a theory of multimolecular adsorption on these lines and showed that the resulting isotherm relation was equivalent to that of B.E.T. He did not postulate adsorption on internal surfaces, but considered adsorption sites distributed throughout the polymer. On these sites, water molecules can combine chemically with the polymer with evolution of heat, one combined molecule to a site, whilst the remaining water exists in a liquid state adjacent to these occupied sites. Cassie's original derivation of the resulting free energy increase in the polymer phase was shown by Hill (*6*) to be incorrect, although the final isotherm relation was correct. What is essentially Hill's derivation is therefore given below.

Suppose there are B moles of adsorption sites per 100 g of wool. Then we first consider the distribution of A moles of water over these sites such that X moles are combined. The remaining $(A-X)$ moles exist in a liquid state with their entropy increased by distributing them over the X occupied sites, allowing any number to each group. We can then write

$$\Delta G_A = \Delta G_X + \Delta G_{(A-X)} \quad \ldots.(16)$$

where ΔG_X is the free-energy change due to the distribution of X moles on B low-energy sites, and $\Delta G_{(A-X)}$ is the free-energy change due to the distribution of $(A-X)$ moles on X occupied sites.

ΔG_X is made up of a heat term, $\Delta H_X = wX$, where w is the heat of reaction between liquid water and the low-energy sites (heat is evolved, so that w is negative), and also an entropy term

$$T.\Delta S_X = RT(\log_e C_X + X.\log_e j_s) \qquad \ldots.(17)$$

where j_s is the partition function for the bound water molecules, and is determined by the number of ways the energy may be distributed amongst the available degrees of freedom. C_X is the number of ways of distributing X moles on B sites, i.e.,

$$C_X = \frac{\lfloor\!\underline{B}}{\lfloor\!\underline{X}\,\lfloor\!\underline{B-X}} = \frac{B^B}{X^X.(B-X)^{(B-X)}} \quad \text{(approximately)}$$

Hence, $\Delta G_X = \Delta H_X - T.\Delta S_X$

$$= -RT[B.\log_e B - X.\log_e X - (B-X).\log_e(B-X) + X\log_e j_s + wX/RT] \ldots.(18)$$

$\Delta G_{(A-X)}$ consists of an entropy term only, similar in form to (17), i.e.,

$$T.\Delta S_{(A-X)} = RT[\log_e C_{(A-X)} + (A-X)\log_e j_L] \quad \ldots.(19)$$

where $C_{(A-X)}$ is the number of ways of distributing $(A-X)$ moles on X sites allowing any number per group.

$$C_{(A-X)} = \frac{\lfloor\!\underline{A}}{\lfloor\!\underline{X}\,\lfloor\!\underline{A-X}} = \frac{A^A}{X^X.(A-X)^{(A-X)}} \quad \text{(approximately)}$$

Therefore,

$$\Delta G_{(A-X)} = -RT[A.\log_e A - X\log_e X - (A-X).\log_e(A-X) + (A-X)\log_e j_L] \ldots..(20)$$

Summing the two terms we obtain the total free-energy change. Then, for equilibrium between the two distributions we determine the condition that ΔG_A is a minimum for a given value of A, i.e., $\frac{\partial \Delta G_A}{\partial X_A} = 0$. The condition is

$$(A-X)(B-X) = \gamma.X^2 \qquad \ldots.(21)$$

where $\gamma = \frac{j_L}{j_s}.e^{w/RT}$.

Now, in order to determine the isotherm relation we equate the chemical potentials of the molecules in the vapour and adsorbed phases, i.e. $\mu_V = \mu_A$, where μ_V, μ_A refer to the vapour and adsorbed phases, respectively. But, assuming the vapour to have the properties of a perfect gas (*7*),

$$\mu_V = \mu_0 + RT.\log_e p \qquad \ldots.(22)$$

where μ_0 is a constant and p the vapour pressure, and

$$\mu_A = \frac{\partial(\Delta G_A)}{\partial A} = RT.\log_e \frac{A-X}{A} - RT.\log_e j_L.$$

Therefore,

$$\mu_0 + RT.\log_e p = RT.\log_e \frac{A-X}{A} - RT.\log_e j_L \qquad \ldots.(23)$$

Also, for equilibrium between a pure liquid and its vapour

$$\mu_0 + RT.\log_e p_s = -RT.\log_e j_L \qquad \ldots.(24)$$

where p_s is the saturation vapour pressure. Therefore,

$$p/p_s = (A-X)/A \qquad \ldots.(25)$$

and, combining this with the equilibrium condition given by equation (21), we obtain the isotherm relation

$$A = \frac{B.p}{(p_s-p)\{\gamma+(1-\gamma)\,p/p_s\}} \qquad \ldots.(26)$$

It should be noted that this is essentially the B.E.T. isotherm, since $A/B = v/v_m$, $C = 1/\beta$ and $a_1 b_2/b_1 a_2 = j_s/j_L$.

Restraints on polymer swelling

The multimolecular adsorption relation as derived thus takes little account of the properties of the adsorbing material, i.e., it assumes that the adsorbent imposes no restriction on the adsorption process. However, for wood, Barkas (*8*) has shown that the energy required to swell the constituent wood cells has a profound effect on the adsorption isotherm. These cells contain a gel substance retained by rigid walls, and in the swollen state the gel is, therefore, subjected to a hydrostatic pressure, which in turn modifies the equilibrium vapour pressure of the adsorbed water.

Cassie (*3*) first estimated the effect of a constraint on adsorption imposed by wool keratin by analogy with Barkas's theory. Assuming the keratin to be an isotropic medium of elastic bulk modulus k, then, if ΔV is the volume increase due to swelling, the corresponding hydrostatic pressure is

$$\Delta P = k.\frac{\Delta V}{V} = \frac{E}{1-2\sigma}.\frac{\Delta r}{r} \qquad \ldots.(27)$$

where V is the volume at zero regain, r is the fibre radius, σ is Poisson's ratio and E is Young's modulus.

When the change in swelling pressure has been estimated thus, the reduction of the observed vapour pressure to that for unconstrained adsorption can be made by means of the usual thermodynamic relation

$$\Delta P = \frac{RT}{V_L} . \log_e \frac{p}{p_u} \qquad \ldots . (28)$$

where p is the observed equilibrium vapour pressure, p_u the vapour pressure for unconstrained adsorption, and V_L the molar volume of the adsorbed water.

Cassie applied these relations to the free isotherm and obtained a 'constrained' isotherm with greatly reduced adsorption (*Figure 40*).

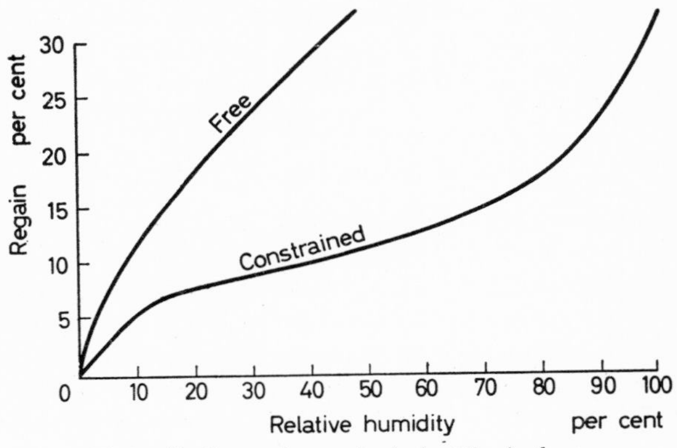

Figure 40. Free and constrained adsorption isotherms

It may then be observed that the sigmoid shape of the constrained isotherm appears to be due largely to the swelling restraint, for the stress-free isotherm has no point of inflexion.

It is perhaps difficult to visualize the existence of a hydrostatic pressure operating on the swollen keratin in the absence of an external restraining sheath as is found in wood cells. Cassie (*4*) later showed, however, that the elastic restraint imposed by keratin was accounted for by introducing an additional heat term in the expression for the free energy of the swollen polymer phase (ΔG_A), i.e.,

$$\Delta G_C = \Delta G_A + \Delta H_E \qquad \ldots . (29)$$

where ΔG_C is the free energy of the constrained polymer phase and ΔH_E the heat absorbed in swelling the gel by the adsorption of A moles of water.

Warburton (*8*) was able to derive an expression for the differential coefficient $\frac{\partial(\Delta H_E)}{\partial A}$ on the assumption that external stresses can produce the same distortions in the wool fibre as those caused by swelling, and by writing

$$\frac{\partial(\Delta H_E)}{\partial A} = RT.\log_e p/p_u \qquad \ldots .(30)$$

the correction for swelling restraint was estimated.

Now, as heat is absorbed in expanding the keratin, for the adsorption of A moles of water the net evolution of heat is not given simply by the product wX. Instead, we must write

$$\Delta H = wX + \Delta H_E$$

and, as ΔH can be obtained from Hedges's (*10*) heat of wetting data, wX may be determined. From the constrained isotherm relation and heat of wetting data, Cassie was able to estimate that

$$B = 1\cdot 1 \text{ moles/100 g keratin}$$
$$w = -3\cdot 5 \text{ kcal/mole.}$$

The number of moles of adsorption sites, B, thus obtained is about equal to the number of average repeat patterns along the polypeptide chain; this led Cassie (*3*) to suggest that the low-energy sites were carbonyl (CO) groups in the main polymer chains. He considered the polar side chains to be relatively unimportant because of the considerable regain shown by silk, which has few such side chains.

Cassie was also able to explain the hysteresis of the wool regain curves in terms of elastic restraint. Barkas had earlier suggested that the hysteresis of sorption isotherms was the result of mechanical hysteresis of the adsorbing gel. We have then

$$\frac{\partial(\Delta H_E)}{\partial A_{AB\text{sorption}}} - \frac{\partial(\Delta H_E)}{\partial A_{DE\text{sorption}}} = RT.\log_e \frac{h_1}{h_2} \qquad \ldots .(31)$$

where h_1 and h_2 refer to the absorption and desorption humidities corresponding to a given regain value.

Further support for the concept of elastic restraint is forthcoming by consideration of the swelling data of Speakman, Stott and Chang (*11*). They showed that wool exhibits a minimum in the temperature–swelling relation at about 37°C (*Figure 41*). The fact that the swelling passes through a minimum indicates that the process is exothermic at temperatures below 37°C and endothermic above this temperature. According to Cassie, this indicates that at first the heat term wX

predominates, but at temperatures above 37°C, ΔH_E is the greater, thus causing a net absorption of heat.

From equations (26) and (30) the constrained adsorption isotherm may be written

$$A = \frac{B}{\left(\frac{p_s}{p}e^{E/RT}-1\right)\left\{\gamma+(1-\gamma)\frac{p}{p_s}e^{-E/RT}\right\}} \qquad \ldots.(32)$$

where $E = \dfrac{\partial(\Delta H_E)}{\partial A}$, and for swelling in water $p = p_s$, so it is possible to obtain a value for E with the condition that $\dfrac{\partial A}{\partial T} = 0$ at 37°C. The value for E, or $\dfrac{\partial(\Delta H_E)}{\partial A}$, thus obtained by Cassie was found to agree with that obtained directly from elastic data (*4*).

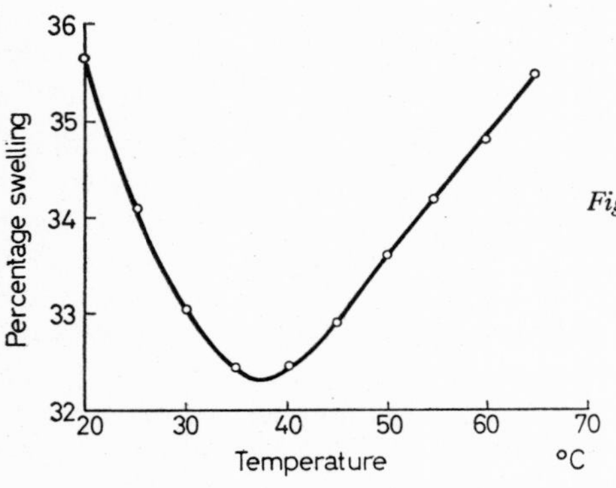

Figure 41. Temperature-swelling relation for Southdown wool

(By courtesy of *J. Text. Inst.*, 1933)

A similar theory of restraint has recently been employed by Newns (*12*) in a study of absorption–desorption kinetics. He suggests that vapour may be absorbed by a polymer in two stages. At first, a quasi-equilibrium is set up with the polymer in a strained state which then relaxes with time.

The free-energy change of the absorbed water due to the temporary restraint ΔG_c is again related to a swelling energy, and we have

$$\frac{\Delta G_c}{V_L} = \Delta P = \delta.\frac{\Delta V}{V} = \frac{RT}{V_L}.\log_e\frac{p}{p_s} \qquad \ldots.(33)$$

where δ is an elastic constant.

It has been suggested that Cassie may be incorrect in his modification of the stress-free isotherm to allow for elastic constraint of the adsorbent, and Gee (*13*), for example, believes that this effect may be small. According to equation (29) we have

$$\Delta G_c = \Delta G_A + \Delta H_E$$

instead of

$$\Delta G_c = \Delta G_A + \Delta G_E \qquad \ldots .(34)$$

$$= \Delta G_A + \Delta H_E - T\Delta S_E \qquad \ldots .(35)$$

where ΔS_E is the entropy change associated with the expansion of the polymer; Cassie assumes this to be negligible. If, however, ΔG_E is small or zero, the original B.E.T. isotherm should fit directly the experimental relation. A reasonable fit is still possible under these conditions provided that B has a smaller value, γ remaining substantially unchanged. A smaller value of B would be consistent with the concept of inaccessible crystalline material in textile polymers.

A further difficulty arises in the determination of $\Delta G_{(A-X)}$. This is derived on the assumption that any number of water molecules may be available in a given cluster, whereas the polymer lattice must impose some limit. Dole (*14*) has considered the case where the number of molecules associated with a site remains finite, and has shown that the isotherm relation then becomes

$$\frac{A}{B} = \frac{x(1+2x+3x^2+\ldots+nx^{n-1})}{(\gamma+x+x^2+\ldots+x^n)} \qquad \ldots .(36)$$

(where n is the maximum number of molecules allowed per cluster, and x is the relative vapour pressure), which is identical with B.E.T. relation for adsorption restricted to n layers. There is, however, no need to assume layer-like adsorption, and the same result is obtained if all the adsorbed molecules have fixed positions relative to one another. In practice it seems likely that some rearrangement of the molecules in a cluster may be possible, but such a refinement may be neglected at the moment.

We have, then, an alternative method of dealing with the adsorption restraint imposed by the lattice of the adsorbent, viz., the introduction of a finite value for n. It may be shown that a rough fit with the wool–water isotherm is still possible for $n = 9$, $B = 0 \cdot 37$ mole/100 g and $\gamma = 0 \cdot 1$; this gives a finite maximum regain of about 33%. It should be noted that, although the maximum number of molecules per cluster is as large as nine, a cluster of this magnitude must occur very infrequently; on the average there will be about four water molecules per cluster at saturation.

ENDERBY'S ADSORPTION THEORY

Taylor (*15*) has recently made a careful check of the water adsorption isotherms for viscose rayon and cotton at regains below about 6%. His results show that neither the B.E.T. nor the Hailwood and Horribin sorption relations fits the isotherm in this range, and this has led Enderby (*16*) to develop an alternative theory in an attempt to account for the discrepancy.

Enderby divides the polymer into cells uniform in size and polymer content. Those in the crystalline regions are considered to be non-adsorbent, so that there remain active cells, all of one type, situated in the amorphous regions of the polymer. In any particular cell there are two types of adsorption site available, viz., primary sites which saturate the bonding potential of the water molecule (*Figure 42*), and secondary sites which, when occupied, provide a similar site for an additional water molecule, any number of sites being allowed. Then, by obtaining the distribution function of the adsorbed water molecules in and amongst the cells, Enderby arrives at an isotherm relation of the form

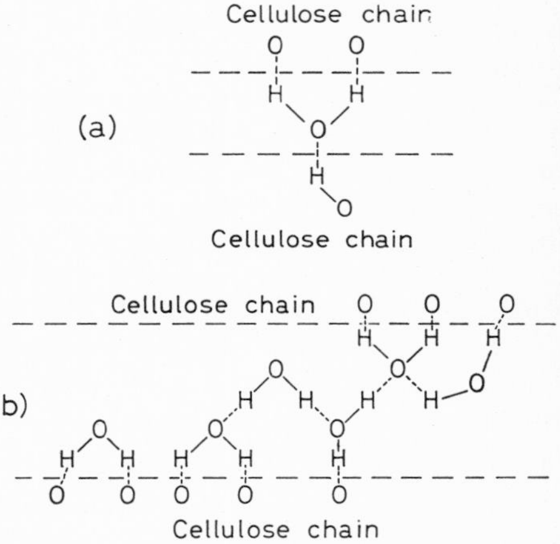

Figure 42. Primary (a) and secondary (b) type sorption of water by cellulose

(By courtesy of *Trans. Faraday Soc.*, 1955)

$$\frac{N}{Q} = \frac{k_1 L}{1 + k_1 L} + \frac{\nu k_2 L}{1 - k_2 L} \qquad \text{....(37)}$$

where N is the total number of adsorbed water molecules, Q the number of cells, and ν the number of secondary sites in a cell.

Also, $k_1 = K_1 \, e^{Eb/RT}$, $k_2 = K_2 \, e^{Ek/RT}$, and $L = p/kT$, where K_1, K_2 are independent of temperature, p is the external water-vapour pressure, k is the Boltzmann constant, and E_b, E_k are the absorption energies for the two types of site.

The relation is then simplified to

$$A = \frac{a.b.p}{1+bp} + Kp \qquad \dots.(38)$$

for $k_2L \ll 1$, where A is the amount of water absorbed, a is related to the weight fraction of amorphous cellulose and the available sites, and b and K are proportional to k_1 and k_2.

This combination of a Langmuir and a linear-type isotherm gave good agreement with Taylor's results for the sorption of water by both viscose rayon and cotton. For viscose rayon, temperature relations gave the molar sorption energies for the primary and secondary sites as 14·4 kcal/mole and 12·7 kcal/mole, respectively. The former value is considered to represent three distorted hydrogen bonds and the latter two hydrogen bonds, which would leave the two remaining hydrogen bonds of the adsorbed water available to bind an additional molecule. The model used gives an adequate representation of the data obtained on viscose rayon, but for cotton energy values were obtained which were difficult to accept. The parameter a was also found to be temperature-dependent.

It is possible to derive an isotherm relation similar to that of Enderby using the methods of Cassie and Hill. Consider adsorption on two types of site:

(*a*) sites that allow only monolayer adsorption,
(*b*) sites that allow multilayer adsorption.

This system is similar in many ways to that discussed by Cassie. Using his notation, we distribute A moles of water such that X moles are distributed over B sites in a monolayer, while the remaining $(A-X)$ moles are distributed on D sites in a multilayer. Then, if w_1, w_2 are the energies of absorption for the two types of sites, respectively, and J_1, J_2 are the corresponding molecular partition functions, we obtain the equilibrium condition

$$\frac{(B-X)\,(A-X)}{X(A-X+D)} \cdot \frac{J_1}{J_2}\, e^{(w_1-w_2)/RT} = 1 \qquad \dots.(39)$$

Then, equating the chemical potential of the vapour and polymer phases, we obtain

$$p = \frac{A-X}{A-X+D} \cdot \frac{e^{-w_2/RT}}{\alpha . J_2} \qquad \dots.(40)$$

where α is related to the partition function of the water vapour and is temperature-dependent.

The isotherm may then be written

$$A = \frac{Bk_1p}{1+k_1p} + \frac{Dk_2p}{1-k_2p} \quad \ldots.(41)$$

where

$$k_1 = J_1 . \alpha . e^{w_1/RT}$$
$$k_2 = J_2 . \alpha . e^{w_2/RT}$$

REFERENCES

1 I. Langmuir, *J. Amer. Chem. Soc.*, **40,** 1361 (1918).
2 S. Brunauer, P. H. Emmett and F. Teller, *J. Amer. Chem. Soc.*, **60,** 309 (1938).
3 A. B. D. Cassie, *Trans. Faraday Soc.*, **41,** 458 (1945).
4 A. B. D. Cassie, *J. Soc. Dyers & Col.*, Symposium 'Fibrous Proteins', 86 (1946).
5 G. A. Gilbert, *J. Soc. Dyers & Col.*, Symposium 'Fibrous Proteins', 96 (1946).
6 T. Hill, *J. Chem. Phys.*, **14,** 263 (1946).
7 R. H. Fowler and E. A. Guggenheim, *Statistical Thermodynamics*, *Cambridge*, 1939, Chap. VIII.
8 W. W. Barkas, *Swelling Stresses in Gels*, Forest Products Lab. Special Report No. 6, H.M.S.O., 1945.
9 F. L. Warburton, *Proc. Phys. Soc.*, **58,** 585 (1946).
10 J. J. Hedges, *Trans. Faraday Soc.*, **22,** 178 (1926).
11 J. B. Speakman, E. Stott and H. Chang, *J. Text. Inst.*, **24,** T284 (1933).
12 A. C. Newns, *Trans. Faraday Soc.*, **52,** 1533 (1956).
13 G. Gee, *Quarterly Reviews*, **1,** 293 (1947).
14 M. Dole, *J. Chem. Phys.*, **16,** 25 (1948).
15 J. Taylor, *J. Text. Inst.*, **45,** T642 (1945).
16 J. A. Enderby, *Trans. Faraday Soc.*, **51,** 106 (1955).

Chapter 7

RATE OF CHANGE OF MOISTURE CONTENT

By J. Crank

When we consider the effect of moisture on textiles, two very obvious questions to ask are: (1) How much moisture can a textile material take up when allowed to come to equilibrium with a humid atmosphere? (2) How quickly does the moisture content change when the textile is transferred to an atmosphere of different humidity? The first question, that of the equilibrium uptake, has been dealt with earlier, and in this and the following two chapters we shall be concerned with the rate at which the moisture content changes and approaches the final equilibrium uptake, that is, with the rate at which a textile is 'conditioned' to the atmosphere surrounding it. Now, it is a well-known property of textiles in general that when moisture is taken up a considerable amount of heat is given out, and vice-versa, and so the study of the exchange of moisture between a textile package and its surroundings and between different parts of the package necessarily involves the study of the changes of temperature and the transfer of heat as well as of moisture. It is the problem of the simultaneous propagation of these two interacting processes—the transfer of moisture and the transfer of heat—with which we are concerned.

PRACTICAL IMPORTANCE OF CONDITIONING TIMES

The rate at which these processes take place is most important from a practical point of view in the textile industry. At various stages of processing, a textile has to be conditioned to a required moisture content; one method of doing this, the so-called 'cellar method' is simply to stand the sample in an atmosphere of the right humidity. The time taken for the moisture content to approach to within a few per cent of the true equilibrium uptake is sometimes prohibitively long. In order to save time, an atmosphere of humidity higher than that required to produce the desired moisture content can be used, and the package removed before equilibrium is reached. If this is to be done successfully, it is essential to know how the moisture content changes with time. Again, it is important to know how long a conditioned package can be left in a room of low humidity between two stages in its processing, without seriously affecting its moisture content. Much the same problem arises in the transporting of bales of cotton, for example. What determines the moisture content of a bale on arrival after shipping across the Atlantic? Does it depend mainly on the conditions under which it was baled or on the conditions of transport? Furthermore, does the moisture content change much from day to day during storage? In testing textile fibres and cloths for physical properties such as breaking load, etc., it is necessary to know how long samples should be left in the conditioning atmo-

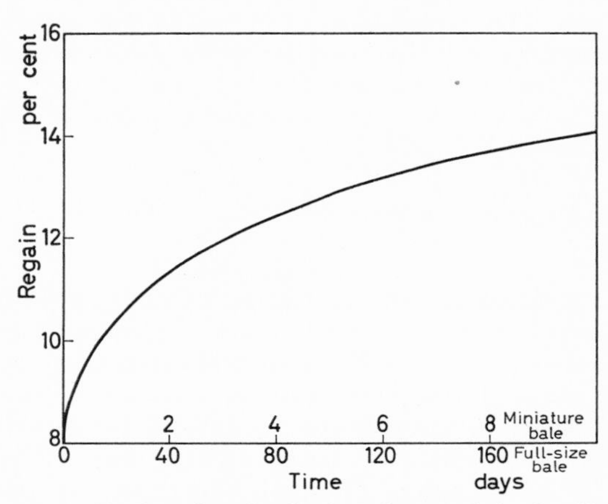

Figure 43. Rate of uptake of moisture by cotton bales placed in a moist atmosphere

sphere before testing and whether the testing needs to be carried out in a conditioned atmosphere or in an ordinary room. This depends on how quickly the moisture content changes. The rates of change are also most important from the point of view of clothing. The fact that they can be, as we shall see, relatively low means that protection against changes of temperature, on going from indoors to outdoors, for example, is afforded for a period which may extend into hours. Finally, the rates of uptake and loss of vapours other than water are important in the manufacture of fibres, for example, in spinning.

Clearly, then, the rate of change is a matter of some practical consequence. Let us consider what happens if we place a textile package in a room in which the relative humidity is kept constant. How does the moisture content change and on what factors does the rate of change depend?

A typical rate of sorption curve

Figure 43 shows the general shape of a rate of uptake curve for a bale of cotton, based on unpublished data supplied by the Shirley Institute. If we use the lower time scale, the curve shows the change in regain of a full-sized bale (roughly 5 ft × 2 ft × 2 ft) initially conditioned to 8% regain and transferred into an atmosphere of higher humidity, which gives an equilibrium regain of 15%. The regain is the moisture content expressed as a percentage of the dry-weight of the bale. The moisture content increases rapidly at first and then changes more and more slowly as the final equilibrium regain of 15% is approached. The simplest way of stating a conditioning time is to give the time necessary to proceed a given fraction of the way to equilibrium. Thus, for the full-sized bale, the time for 50% of the final change in moisture content to occur is about 40 days, and for 90% about 240 days.

FACTORS CONTROLLING CONDITIONING TIME

Size

If we may anticipate a little, mathematical investigation shows that the time taken to reach a given fraction of the final regain is proportional to the square of the linear dimensions of a bale, if the shape remains the same. The figures for the miniature bale were obtained by direct observation and those for the full-sized bale were deduced by this square law. With this adjustment of time scale, the same curve applies to both bales. Thus, if a miniature bale is constructed with dimensions one-fifth of those of a normal bale it will go through its changes 25 times as quickly as the big bale, though otherwise its regain follows the same course. This is a most useful rule in practice because it enables conditioning times for a large bale to be deduced from those for a small bale, whereas experiments on a large bale would be prohibitively long and expensive. This was partly the reason for undertaking the mathematical work in the first instance. We shall see later that the rate of sorption depends to some extent on the average regain, but for most practical purposes the curve can be taken as applying to any regain.

Shape

The first factor influencing the rate of conditioning, therefore, is size, i.e., the dimensions of a package, the weight of a cloth, the diameter or count of a yarn or fibre. Shape is also important. Unpublished information on conditioning times for the following packages has been supplied by the Shirley Institute: roving bobbin, ring tube, mule cop, bottle bobbin, warper's bobbin, cone, cheese, skip of cops, warper's beam, weaver's beam, bale of raw cotton. These were conditioned to 33% r.h. and then moved to 65% r.h. at 65–70°F. The times taken to reach a regain half-way between the initial and final ones range from 3 hours for a mule cop to 40 days for a bale of cotton; corresponding times for 90% conditioning are 12 hours and 3 months. Conditioning times for cloths are of the order of minutes and for rovings and coarse yarns, of seconds.

Density

The other property of the package itself which is important is the density, which governs the permeability of the package to water vapour. The permeability is lower the more compressed, i.e. the denser, the package, and so conditioning times are longer for a dense package. For most purposes the conditioning time can be taken as directly proportional to the density of the package.

Textile

We must expect also, of course, that conditioning times will vary for different textile materials, cotton, wool, silk, rayons, etc.

So much for the properties of the package itself. The rate of conditioning is also markedly dependent on two properties of the conditioning atmosphere. The first is temperature and the second is the degree of circulation of the air or the freedom of access of the air to the surface of the package.

Temperature

If the relative humidity is kept constant, a rise in temperature of 20°F will roughly halve the conditioning time and a rise of 40°F will quarter it. This provides a useful means, in some cases, of speeding up the conditioning process, but it must be remembered that the moisture content of the textile is *mainly* determined by the *relative* humidity and to keep this constant as the temperature rises calls for an addition of moisture to the conditioning atmosphere.

Air circulation

The figures that have been quoted so far are based on the assumption that the air has free access to the surface of the package and is freely circulating. This is important, particularly for small packages and cloths, because, as the package takes up moisture, the air in contact with its surface will be partially denuded of water and the conditioning of the package will be delayed unless the air currents are sufficient to maintain a supply of moist air to the surface. This is not likely to be important for a large bale but may be so for small samples where the uptake is more rapid. To quote one example from work carried out at the Shirley Institute, it was found that a cloth (23 oz duck) exposed to a still atmosphere in a conditioning box took three times as long to condition as when placed in the draught from a fan. In obtaining the figures already quoted, there was moderate circulation of the air around the packages, which were suspended in an air-conditioned room fitted with a circulating fan.

Average regain

The conditioning time depends strictly on the average regain of the package, being longer at very low and very high regains and shorter at intermediate regains. Over the range of regains of most practical interest, however, the conditioning time can usually be taken to be independent of regain.

With the aid of Table 8, p. 88, the combined effect of these various factors is readily determined approximately. This table, hitherto unpublished, is reproduced here with the kind permission of the Director of the Shirley Institute, where it was originally compiled. It shows correction factors to be applied to the conditioning time for a standard package under standard conditions in order to estimate the time required to condition any other package under specified conditions. The desired time is obtained simply by multiplying the basic half-way period of 12 hours by the various factors successively.

STAGES IN MOISTURE TRANSFER

It is convenient to think of the transfer of moisture from the atmosphere to the package as taking place in three distinct stages, though in practice they occur simultaneously. They are:

(1) Passage of moisture from the surrounding air to the surface of the package. As we have said, this may be important for small packages in still air, but by circulating the air this stage can be made effectively instantaneous.
(2) Passage of moisture from the surface to the interior of the package. A package consists of a number of individual fibres of cotton or wool, etc., packed together but with air spaces in between. Moisture enters the package by diffusion, mainly through the air, though some moisture may pass along the fibres themselves (*1*, *2*).
(3) Absorption of moisture by the individual fibres from the air between them, as moisture diffuses radially into the fibres.

Step 3 is accompanied by the evolution of heat and this affects the relative humidity of the air and hence the ability of the fibres to

TABLE 8

TABLE OF CORRECTION FACTORS TO STANDARD HALF-WAY PERIOD OF 12 HOURS

Size and shape of package	Density		Nature of material		Average regain		Temperature		Approach	
	oz/in³	Factor	Material	Factor	% Regain	Factor	°F	Factor	%	Factor
	0·05	$\frac{1}{6}$	Cotton (unmercerized)	1	Dry	6	40	$2\frac{1}{2}$	5	$\frac{1}{60}$
	0·1	$\frac{1}{3}$	Cotton (mercerized)	$1\frac{1}{4}$	1	2	50	$1\frac{3}{4}$	10	$\frac{1}{20}$
$\left(\frac{2 \times \text{volume of package}}{\text{surface area}}\right)^2$	0·2	$\frac{2}{3}$	Viscose rayon	2	2	1	60	$1\frac{1}{4}$	20	$\frac{1}{6}$
	0·3	1	Cuprammonium rayon		4	$\frac{2}{3}$	70	$\frac{3}{4}$	30	$\frac{1}{3}$
	0·4	$1\frac{1}{3}$	(Bemberg)	$1\frac{3}{4}$	6	$\frac{3}{4}$	80	$\frac{1}{2}$	40	$\frac{2}{3}$
			Fortisan	$1\frac{2}{3}$	7	1	90	$\frac{1}{3}$	50	1
			Cellulose acetate	$1\frac{1}{4}$	8	$1\frac{1}{4}$			60	$1\frac{1}{2}$
			Silk (raw)	$1\frac{1}{2}$	10	2			70	2
All measurements in inches			Silk (degummed)	$1\frac{1}{2}$	12	3			80	3
			Nylon	$\frac{2}{3}$	14	5			90	6
									95	8
									99	14

absorb, not only where the heat is released, but throughout the package, as the heat itself diffuses through the air spaces and along the fibres. The considerable progress that has been made in the theoretical and mathematical treatment of this very complicated problem of the simultaneous transfer of heat and moisture is due very largely to the realization that individual fibres can be considered to be always in equilibrium with the air immediately surrounding them. We must therefore look at the reasoning which led to this conclusion and at the experimental evidence in its support.

SORPTION BY A SINGLE FIBRE

Water penetrates individual fibres by diffusion. To make reliable diffusion measurements on a single fibre is difficult, but for wool the rate of diffusion can be deduced from measurements on keratin. Keratin is closely similar to wool both physically and chemically and it is more convenient to measure diffusion rates into a relatively large sheet of keratin than into a wool fibre. The general subject of diffusion in fibre-forming substances is dealt with more fully later. All we need to know at the moment is that, for regains of the magnitude of those with which we are concerned, a diffusion coefficient of 10^{-7} cm^2/s can be taken as representative. The time for a single fibre to reach, say, 80% of its final uptake of moisture depends not only on the diffusion coefficient, but also on the diameter of the fibre—the thinner the fibre the more quickly it absorbs. Now, the average diameter of a textile fibre is so small (rather less than 10^{-3} cm) that for a diffusion coefficient of 10^{-7} cm^2/s 80% absorption will be attained in about 2 seconds. This is so small compared with the conditioning times, ranging from hours to months for the packages we have already referred to, that we are justified in saying that an individual fibre reaches equilibrium with its immediate surroundings instantaneously.

King and Cassie (*3*) attempted to demonstrate this conclusion experimentally by measuring the rate of absorption of water vapour by a small mass of wool (0·25 g) suspended from a sensitive spring-balance in an evacuated chamber into which water vapour was introduced at 23·5 mm pressure. The apparatus was housed in a thermostat at 25°C and so the final regain should have been about 30%. By suspending the wool in an evacuated chamber, King and Cassie eliminated diffusion through any surrounding atmosphere and they expected to measure directly a rate of uptake governed solely by diffusion within the fibres. From what has just been said we would expect the absorption to take only a few seconds. This does not appear at first sight to be supported by the regain–time curve observed experimentally, which reaches 80% uptake only after an hour or so (*Figure 44*).

We must remember, however, that when the water vapour is absorbed by the wool a large amount of heat is evolved, which produces a considerable increase in the temperature of the fibres. The temperature observed in the experiment is shown in *Figure 45*. It was obtained by winding fine platinum wire into the wool and using this

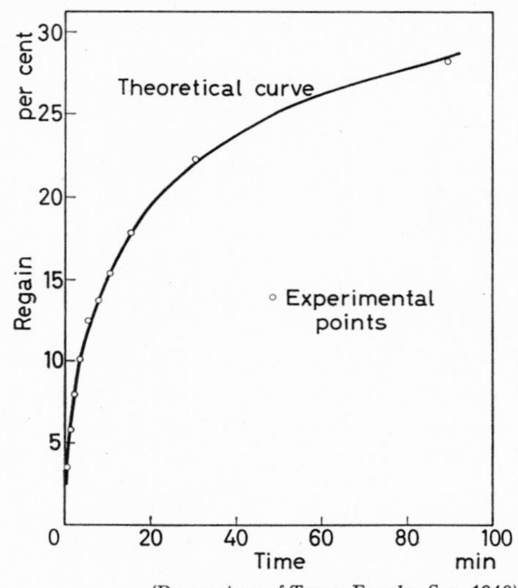

(By courtesy of *Trans. Faraday Soc.*, 1940)

Figure 44. Rate of uptake of moisture by wool fibres in vacuum

as a resistance thermometer. King and Cassie showed that, when this rise in temperature is taken into account, the relatively slow rate of sorption observed can be reconciled with the statement that an individual fibre reaches equilibrium with its surroundings effectively instantaneously.

Their argument is as follows. The regain of a textile depends on the vapour pressure and also on the temperature of its atmosphere; the regain is greater the higher the vapour pressure, but is decreased by a rise in temperature. In a subsidiary experiment, King and Cassie (*3*) measured the regain at 25°C at various vapour pressures. In the experiment we have described, the wool was originally at 25°C and water vapour at 23·5 mm pressure was suddenly introduced. Their observations of the effect on regain of vapour pressure showed that, if the temperature of the wool remained at 25°C, its regain would be more than 30%. But, because the temperature rises to more than 65°C, the regain immediately acquired is much less than 30%. If we assume the wool to come to equilibrium with its surroundings immediately, so that there is no time for any heat to be lost, the initial regain and temperature can easily be calculated. First, King and Cassie calculated the regain for different temperatures at the pressure of the experiment by applying Kirchoff's law to their observations of the relation between regain and pressure at

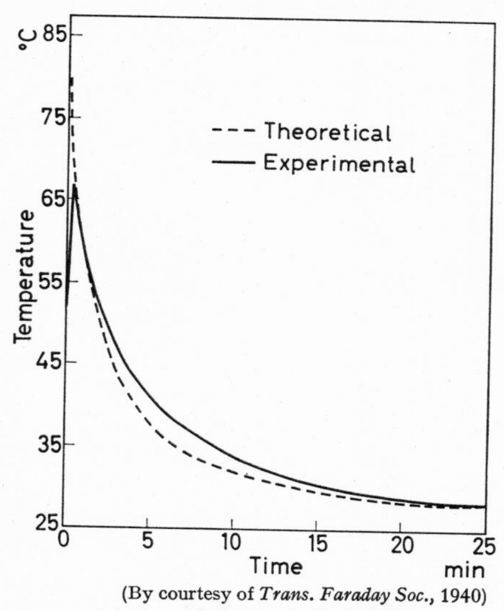

(By courtesy of *Trans. Faraday Soc.*, 1940)

Figure 45. Temperature change resulting from absorption of water vapour by wool fibres in vacuum

25°C. They obtained a curve (*Figure 46*) showing what the regain of the wool is in the experiment when in equilibrium with any given temperature, i.e., there is one relationship between regain and temperature to be satisfied at equilibrium. But, the change in temperature is produced by the change in regain. It is, in fact, directly proportional to the heat evolved, i.e., to the change in regain.

Thus, if the fractional regain immediately acquired by the wool is α, the heat evolved in 1 g of initially dry wool is αq, where q is the heat of absorption per gram of water vapour. If the specific heat of the wool is f, the temperature (T) produced by a regain α is given by

$$T - T_0 = \alpha q / f$$

where T_0, the initial temperature, is 25°C in this example. This is the second relation between temperature and regain, giving the straight line in *Figure 46*. Both relationships are satisfied at the intersection of the two curves of *Figure 46* and the regain and temperature immediately acquired can be read off. They are roughly 2·3% regain and 80°C. Thus, even though the conditions of the experiment are such that a regain of 30% is ultimately attained by the wool, it cannot increase instantaneously by more than 2·3% even if diffusion of water vapour into the fibre is infinitely rapid. Experimental observations of temperatures (*Figure 45*) do not give a point much

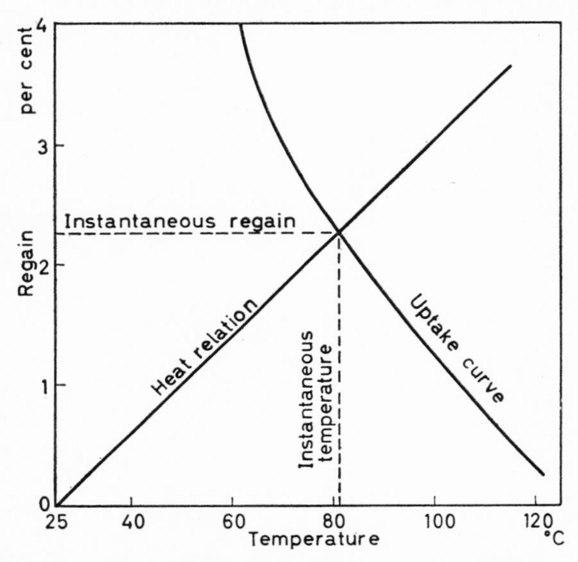

Figure 46. Determination of immediate equilibrium of fibres in vacuum

higher than 65°C, but this was observed after 30 seconds, and if allowance is made for some inevitable cooling it is not inconsistent with the calculated figure of 80°C.

As the cooling proceeds, the regain steadily increases; King and Cassie (*3*) calculated the regain–time curve to be expected, assuming the wool to be always in equilibrium with the water vapour–temperature conditions around it and assuming Newton's law of cooling. Both the cooling curve (*Figure 45*) and the regain–time curve (*Figure 44*) are shown to agree well with experiment. The one adjustable parameter in the calculation of the cooling curve is the emissivity, and this has a reasonable value when compared with standard measurements of emissivity.

The assumption of instantaneous equilibrium for individual fibres is thus seen to be justified, but in calculating the rate of sorption due account must be taken of heat and temperature changes. On this basis we can proceed to give an account of the propagation of heat and moisture through a textile package.

REFERENCES

1 F. T. Peirce, W. H. Rees and L. W. Ogden, *J. Text. Inst.*, **36,** T169 (1945).
2 S. Baxter, *J. Text. Inst.*, **37,** T39 (1946).
3 G. King and A. B. D. Cassie, *Trans. Faraday Soc.*, **36,** 445 (1940).

CHAPTER 8

SIMULTANEOUS DIFFUSION OF HEAT AND MOISTURE

By J. Crank

REACTION OF TEXTILE TO ATMOSPHERIC CHANGE

In Chapter 7 we saw how a mass of fibres, suspended in a vacuum, responded to the sudden introduction of water vapour to the space around them. The immediate reaction of the fibres when presented to a new atmosphere is to attempt to modify that atmosphere until equilibrium is reached, without a large change in their own moisture content. The fibres do this by increasing the temperature of the atmosphere, thereby lowering the relative humidity. This is possible because a large amount of heat is evolved even for a small change in the regain of the fibres. Only later, as this heat is lost and the temperature falls, does the moisture content of the fibres slowly increase, finally reaching equilibrium with the new atmosphere of high relative humidity and the original temperature. This experiment in a vacuum may seem artificial, but it does illustrate the characteristic behaviour of a textile, which is to oppose, at first, any change in its atmosphere.

Consider now an example quoted by Cassie (*1*) having a more direct bearing on practical affairs. Suppose a sheet of wool fibres conditioned to 45% r.h. at 20°C, so that its regain is 10%, is suddenly placed in a stream of air at 65% r.h. and the same temperature.

The wool and air can come to equilibrium in two very different ways:

(1) by an increase in the regain of the wool until it is in equilibrium, when a regain of 14% obtains; or

(2) by an increase in the temperature of the wool and air until the new water-vapour pressure represents only 45% r.h., the regain of the wool remaining essentially unchanged at 10%. It is easy to calculate from vapour pressure tables that this will be so if the temperature rises to 26°C.

Of these two possible equilibrium conditions the first, as we have said, involving a considerable change in regain, can be achieved only after a large volume of air has passed through the wool. The second, involving a temperature rise, is easily attained almost immediately, because of the large heat of sorption. Enough heat is produced by a relatively small increase in regain to raise the temperature of the wool to 26°C ($\frac{1}{4}$% is adequate, neglecting for the moment the heat capacity of air). For this reason, the first equilibrium set up is the one in which the temperature rises but the regain is essentially unchanged. This is only a pseudo-equilibrium, however, because if we continue to blow air at 20°C over the wool the final temperature must be 20°C and the final regain 14%. Here we have the essential feature of the propagation of humidity and temperature changes in textiles, namely, the existence of two equilibrium states—a temporary one set up quickly and involving no change in regain, and a permanent one set up relatively slowly and involving a regain change. This argument is somewhat oversimplified because we have neglected the fact that a good deal of heat is carried away by the air, and also that, not only is the relative humidity of the air decreased by a rise in temperature, but also its moisture content decreases because the air gives up some moisture to the wool as it passes through. This is a small amount from the wool's point of view but may be appreciable from the point of view of the air.

Let us look a little more carefully at the problem. Let the wool be conditioned at first to an atmosphere of temperature T_0 and moisture content C_0. In our example $T_0 = 20$°C; $C_0 = 8 \cdot 35 \times 10^{-6}$ g/cm³ for a r.h. of 45%. Let the incident air be specified by T_0, C_1 (in the present example $C_1 = 12 \cdot 0 \times 10^{-6}$ g/cm³) and the emergent air by T_2, C_2. This is a simple case in which the wool is presented with a change in relative humidity but not of temperature. As C_1 is greater than C_0, moisture is taken up by the wool and the heat evolved by the wool must equal that gained by the air in passing through. If q is the heat evolved when 1 g of water vapour is absorbed by the wool, the heat given out by the wool when 1 cm³ of air passes is $q(C_1 - C_2)$. The heat gained by the 1 cm³ of air is $\rho c(T_2 - T_0)$, where ρ is the density and c the specific heat of the air. The heat capacity of the wool can be neglected in comparison with q. Thus we have the equation for the balance of heat

$$q(C_1 - C_2) = \rho c(T_2 - T_0) \qquad \ldots.(1)$$

Also, since the regain of the wool is considered to be unchanged, the atmospheres specified by T_0, C_0 and T_2, C_2 are both in equilibrium with the same regain and therefore must satisfy Kirchoff's equation. A convenient form of this is

$$C_2 - C_0 = \frac{qC_0}{R(T+273)^2}(T_2 - T_0) \qquad \ldots.(2)$$

where R is the gas constant per gram of water. From these two relationships we can calculate T_2 and C_2. For the example we have discussed, Cassie (*1*) found

$$C_2 = 10{\cdot}4 \times 10^{-6} \text{ g/cm}^3$$
$$T_2 = 23{\cdot}7^\circ\text{C}.$$

Thus, roughly only half the concentration change occurs immediately, the rest coming later as the regain changes.

The other simple case is that in which the wool is presented with a change of temperature but not of vapour pressure. Here the immediate equilibrium is achieved by evaporation of moisture from the wool and a simultaneous drop in temperature of the air. Now we have air incident at T_1,C_0 and the heat-exchange equation is

$$q(C_2 - C_0) = \rho c(T_1 - T_2) \qquad \ldots.(3)$$

Using Kirchoff's equation again, we can calculate T_2,C_2. In a further example quoted by Cassie (*1*), the air temperature is increased from 20°C to 35°C ($T_0 = 20$, $T_1 = 35$), the water content remaining at $10{\cdot}5 \times 10^{-6}$ g/cm³, which corresponds to 60% r.h. at 20°C. We find then

$$T_2 = 26^\circ\text{C}$$
$$C_2 = 14{\cdot}5 \times 10^{-6} \text{ g/cm}^3.$$

We see that here also only half the *temperature* change occurs immediately. We should notice that, as Cassie stresses, the temperature acquired by the air at first is largely determined by the properties of the air. Heat of absorption, q, is the only factor associated with the textile and this, being roughly the latent heat of water, does not vary much from one textile to another. The textile is in fact merely a means whereby constant relative humidity is preserved. It so happens that the amount of heat required to evaporate into 1 litre of air enough moisture to maintain a constant relative humidity, when the temperature is increased by 1°C, is roughly equal to the heat obtained by cooling 1 litre of dry air through 1°C. It is the equality of these two factors acting in opposite ways that produces the half-way temperature of 26°C. In this way clothing offers temporary protection against changes of humidity and temperature.

Baxter and Cassie (*2*) carried out an experiment to check these ideas of the propagation of a temperature change through a textile. They used a hollow cylinder (*Figure 47*) made entirely of textiles, through which air could be forced mechanically. The outer and inner walls were made of woven starched linen and between these walls fibres were packed. This textile cylinder was housed in an outer brass cylinder which could be transferred rapidly from a thermostat at 20°C to one at 35°C. Air entered through the opening E in the outer cylinder and then filtered through the textiles to escape through the hollow centre of the inner cylinder. Thermocouples T_1,

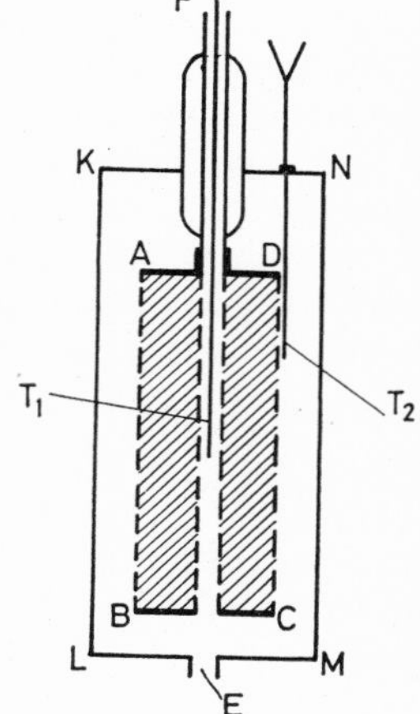

Figure 47. Apparatus for studying propagation of temperature change through textiles
(By courtesy of *Trans. Faraday Soc.*, 1940)

T_2 measured the temperature of the air before and after passing through the textile cylinder. The water-vapour concentration of the incident air was maintained at $10 \cdot 5 \times 10^{-6}$ g/cm³ throughout the

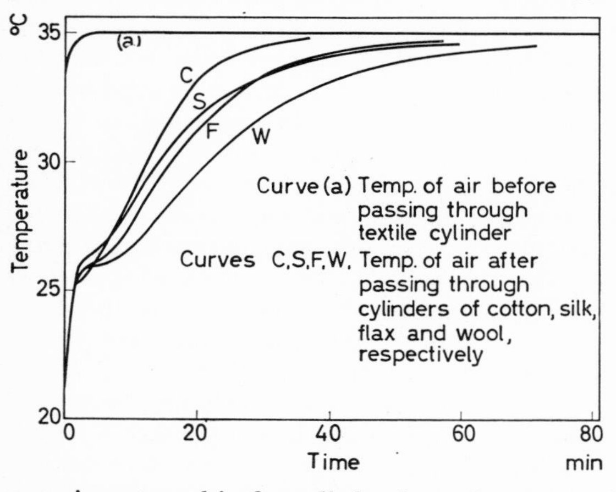

Figure 48. Temperature variation at centre of textile cylinder on passage of moist air
(By courtesy of *Trans. Faraday Soc.*, 1941)

experiment, and in fact all the data of our second calculation above were those of the experiment.

Temperature–time curves for different natural fibres are shown in *Figure 48*. They all show a rapid increase in temperature of the air emerging from the textile from 20 to 26°C, there being only minor differences for different fibres. This is in very good agreement with the calculations. There is then a slow drift of temperature towards the final figure of 35°C.

PROPAGATION OF TWO DISTURBANCES

We have so far referred only to the condition of the air as it leaves the textile. Clearly, however, when the air first passes through, a front, separating the original and pseudo-equilibrium conditions, moves through the textile with the speed of the air-flow, if we neglect the heat capacity of the textile. Between this front and the outside of the textile cylinder, where the air is incident, the changes we have discussed will have taken place and the intermediate temperature and concentration will have been set up, while between the front and the inner surface of the cylinder the original conditions prevail. Thus, we have a fast disturbance representing change of temperature and water-vapour content without change of regain, followed by a much slower disturbance bringing a change of regain.

So far we have considered air being forced through the mass of textile. It has been useful to do this because it is somewhat easier to think about than the case in which the air penetrates merely by diffusion. It is fairly clear, however, that the same general behaviour is to be expected in the diffusion case; if a textile package, conditioned to certain atmospheric conditions, is suddenly transferred to a different atmosphere, moisture and temperature changes will be propagated through the textile by diffusion in the form of two disturbances, a fast one involving temperature and concentration changes only and a change of regain following at a slower rate of propagation.

Mathematical equations describing these phenomena in detail have been developed from which it is possible to calculate how concentration, temperature and regain vary with time at any point of the textile mass till final equilibrium is attained. Henry (*3*) gave the theory for diffusion of humid air into a textile package, and Cassie (*4*) later put forward the corresponding theory for air forced through the package, neglecting diffusion effects entirely. Since then Daniels (*5*) has taken into account diffusion of heat and moisture in an air stream forced through the package. More recently, Henry (*6*) has extended his early work and given numerical values of parameters appearing in the theory so that, for the cases he considers, it is a relatively simple matter to calculate how moisture and temperature changes penetrate a given package. The following treatment is based essentially on Henry's work.

EQUATIONS FOR DIFFUSION OF HEAT AND MOISTURE

1. *Equilibrium equation*

Figure 49 shows diagrammatically an element of a textile package (occupied partly by fibres and partly by air spaces). This is much over-simplified, but serves to fix ideas. We have said that a fibre can always be considered as being in equilibrium with its immediate surroundings. We shall further assume linear dependence on both temperature and moisture content and write

$$M = \text{constant} + aC - bT \qquad \ldots.(4)$$

where C is the concentration of water vapour in the air spaces (g/cm³), M is the amount of moisture absorbed by unit mass of fibre, and a and b are constants. We shall consider the equilibrium uptake of moisture by a fibre to be related to water-vapour concentration and

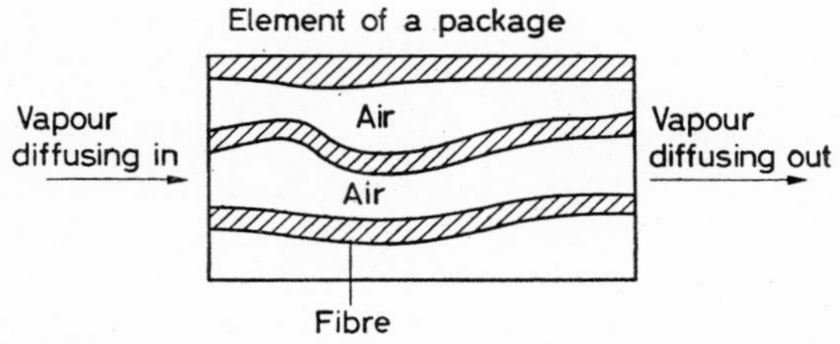

Figure 49. Diagrammatic representation of element of textile package

temperature T by the relation given in equation (4). This is a necessary assumption if the theory is to proceed; clearly, in practice it is only an approximation which is reasonable over small ranges of humidity and temperature.

2. *Vapour diffusion equation*

Consider the element of a textile package. We can derive two equations, one expressing the rate of change of concentration and the other the rate of change of temperature.

The rate of change of concentration is governed by:

(*a*) Diffusion of vapour through the air spaces and through the fibres, both these being proportional to the concentration gradient in the usual way. Diffusion through the pores will in many cases be greater than through the fibres, but even if this is not so we can represent both processes by one term if we assume that the vapour in the fibre is always in equilibrium with that in the air in the immediate neighbourhood and that the absorption isotherm is linear as in equation (4).

(*b*) The absorption or desorption of moisture by the fibres from the air spaces.

Thus, we can say,

Net amount of vapour entering element by diffusion
= increase in moisture in air
+ increase in moisture in fibres ....(5)

If a fraction v of the total volume of the package is occupied by air and $1-v$ by fibre of density ρ_s, the equation governing the movement of vapour, expressing equation (5) mathematically can be written

$$vgD_A \frac{\partial^2 C}{\partial x^2} = \frac{v\partial C}{\partial t} + (1-v)\,\rho_s \frac{\partial M}{\partial t} \qquad \text{....(6)}$$

where C and M have already been defined and D_A is the diffusion coefficient for moisture in air. The factor g allows for the fact that diffusion is not along straight air channels, but through a matrix of intertwined fibres; any diffusion along the fibres themselves can also be allowed for in this factor, which can be determined from permeability measurements under steady-state conditions.

3. *Heat diffusion equation*

The rate at which the temperature of the element changes is determined by:

(*a*) conduction of heat through air and fibres,
(*b*) the heat evolved when moisture is absorbed by fibres.

Thus

Increase in heat content of fibres
= net amount of heat entering by conduction
+ heat evolved as fibres absorb moisture ....(7)

and this is expressed mathematically by the equation

$$c\rho \frac{\partial T}{\partial t} = K \frac{\partial^2 T}{\partial x^2} + q\rho \frac{\partial M}{\partial t} \qquad \text{....(8)}$$

where c is the specific heat of the fibres, K the heat conductivity of the package, ρ the density of the package (expressed as mass of fibre per unit over-all volume), and q is the heat evolved when 1 g of water vapour is absorbed by the fibres. In writing equation (8) the reasonable assumption has been made that the heat content of the air is negligible compared with that of the fibres.

One vital point to notice is that both equation (6) and equation (8), the vapour equation and the temperature equation, involve M, the amount of moisture in the fibres. It is at once obvious that the two processes, the transfer of moisture and the transfer of heat, are coupled together in this way and that we cannot in general consider one process without considering the other simultaneously.

ASSUMPTIONS UNDERLYING THE MATHEMATICAL THEORY

It is worth while to enumerate some of the assumptions on which the theoretical treatment is based. The main ones are:

(*a*) The linear dependence of M on C and T, to which reference has already been made, is assumed.

(*b*) The quantities D_A, K, c and ρ are assumed constant and independent of moisture concentration and temperature.

(*c*) The heat of sorption q is assumed independent of regain, though in practice it is not.

(*d*) Hysteresis of sorption is neglected, i.e., the equilibrium equation (equation (4)) is assumed to hold whether the fibre is gaining or losing moisture.

(*e*) The relative volumes occupied by fibre and air are assumed not to change as diffusion proceeds, i.e., v is assumed constant. In fact, as the fibres sorb moisture they swell and occupy progressively more space, and the air correspondingly less. This effect is thought to be unimportant except for very dense packages.

(*f*) No account has been taken of the influence of capillarity in the air spaces. This will be appreciable only at very high humidities or in water.

(*g*) The fibres have been assumed to reach equilibrium with their immediate surroundings instantaneously. There is some evidence that relatively slow changes of fibre structure may occur as the moisture is taken up, and that while most of the uptake is effectively instantaneous there may be a slow drift of moisture content persisting for some time. The information on this at the moment is too sparse for it to be taken into account even if the mathematics permitted.

PHYSICAL SIGNIFICANCE OF THE MATHEMATICAL SOLUTIONS

Henry (*3*) obtained mathematical solutions of the above equations showing how concentration, temperature and total moisture content vary with time at any place in a textile package. His solutions show that, when the conditions of the atmosphere surrounding a package are changed, moisture and heat diffuse in or out until the package reaches a new equilibrium, and that both moisture and temperature changes may be considered to be the result of two disturbances or waves moving through the package independently and at different rates. For example, the total moisture change can be considered as the sum of two disturbances travelling independently, and each moisture wave is accompanied by a temperature wave, moving at the same rate, whose magnitude is proportional to that of the moisture wave, the relation between the two depending on the properties of the textile package. Alternatively, we may think of two temperature waves moving at different speeds, each accompanied by a moisture wave. In other words, the two processes are 'coupled' together. When the speeds of the two waves are calculated for textile packages under practical conditions of humidity and temperature, one wave is found to move very quickly and one very slowly. In fact, we find what we have already seen from simple theory, that rapid changes of moisture concentration in the air spaces and of temperature, which do not involve appreciable change of regain, are followed by a slow change in the moisture content of the fibres.

THE MATHEMATICAL SOLUTIONS

Let us look at the solutions in their simplest form for the case of most direct interest to our general subject, namely that in which a dry textile package is placed in a humid atmosphere of the same temperature as the package. For this case Henry (*6*) has written the solutions very simply. The equation for the concentration of moisture in the air spaces in the package is

$$C/C_0 = (1-H)f_1 + pf_2 \qquad \ldots .(9)$$

where C_0 is the final equilibrium concentration. The f_1 and f_2 are functions of position in the package and of time, which we shall discuss in a moment. They depend only on the shape and size of the package. Here f_1 is associated with one wave, f_2 with the other, and from equation (9) the resultant change in concentration is seen to be obtained by adding the two waves. H is a complicated function of the properties of the textile and the package, which depends also on the humidity and temperature conditions of the atmosphere. The quantities appearing in H have already been introduced through equations (4), (6) and (8). They are D_A, K, g, c, ρ, ρ_s, a, b and q. The way in which these quantities appear is given in Henry's paper and Henry has presented also a table of numerical values of H for three mean relative humidities, three temperatures and two densities of cotton package. Nomograms are also given from which values of H for other conditions can readily be calculated for cotton.

The solution for temperature is

$$T - T_0 = C_0 s(f_1 - f_2) \qquad \ldots .(10)$$

and for total moisture content

$$M/M_0 = (1+n)f_1 - nf_2 \qquad \ldots .(11)$$

where T_0 is the initial temperature, M_0 the final moisture content at equilibrium and n and s are parameters, being different functions of the variables involved in H. Values of n are given also by Henry (*6*) to correspond with those of H.

The functions f_1 and f_2

These are two functions associated with the two waves of which we have spoken, f_1 referring to the slow wave and f_2 to the fast, and the speeds at which these disturbances diffuse through the package are determined by two diffusion constants D_1 and D_2, respectively. These are given as the roots of a quadratic equation in the theory and values are tabulated by Henry. Then, f_1 is the solution to the problem of simple diffusion or simple heat conduction into the package being studied when the diffusion constant is D_1, i.e., it is the solution of Fick's equation or the simple heat conduction equation; f_2 is the same solution with D_1 replaced by D_2. If we wish to know how M, for example, varies with time at a given point in the package, it is through f_1 and f_2 that the coordinates of the point and time are introduced. If we are interested only in the *total moisture* content of the whole package, however, the fs are functions only of time. As an example, suppose that the package is in the form of a large flat sheet; from any standard textbook on diffusion or heat conduction (*7, 8*) we find

$$f_1 = 1 - \frac{8}{\pi^2}\left(1 + e^{-m} + \frac{1}{9}e^{-9m} + \frac{1}{25}e^{-25m} \ldots\right) \qquad \ldots .(12)$$

where $m = \pi^2 D_1 t/l^2$, l being the thickness of the sheet. The function f_2 is the same with D_1 replaced by D_2. Corresponding functions for other shapes of package can be found in the textbooks. We see, therefore, that this complicated problem of the simultaneous transfer of heat and moisture has been reduced to a problem in simple heat conduction. A shortened account of Henry's work which includes the basic relationships, nomograms and tables of numerical values is given in a book by Crank (*8*).

Comments on Solutions

The following points about the solutions are of particular interest:

(*a*) Since both f_1 and f_2 always vary between 0 to 1, we see from equation (10) that the change in temperature, associated with an initial change of vapour pressure only, is a transient one, which increases from zero to a maximum and disappears again. This transient temperature change has been observed by Cassie and Baxter (*2*).

(*b*) If the initial disturbance is one of temperature only, there is a corresponding transient change in moisture content which for practical reasons is more difficult to observe experimentally.

(*c*) The effect of size or shape is all included in the *f*s and so the conversion from one package to another of different size and shape is relatively simple. In particular, t and l always appear as t/l^2, as in equation (12), leading immediately to the dependence on the square of the linear dimensions which we have already discussed.

COMPARISON OF THEORY AND EXPERIMENT

Cassie and Baxter (*2*) measured the temperature variation at the centre of their textile cylinder, after suitably modifying the apparatus

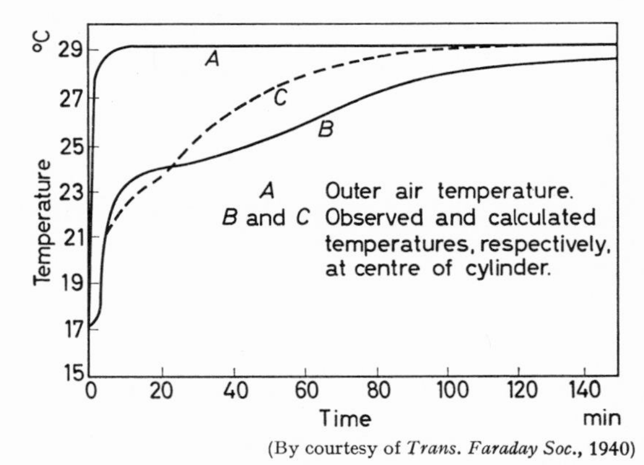

(By courtesy of *Trans. Faraday Soc.*, 1940)

Figure 50. Temperature variation at centre of textile cylinder on passage of moist air (diffusion experiment)

for a diffusion instead of a flow experiment. They compared the observed temperatures at various times with those calculated from the above equations. *Figure 50* shows that the theory accounts for the general features, though the agreement is not as good as for the flow-under-pressure measurements when these are compared with Daniel's calculations (*5*) allowing for diffusion in the air stream (*Figure 51*). This is probably due to the difficulty of determining the relevant diffusion coefficients required in the calculations of the diffusion case.

It is not to be expected that the theoretical treatment of a subject as complicated as this can reproduce all the features accurately and

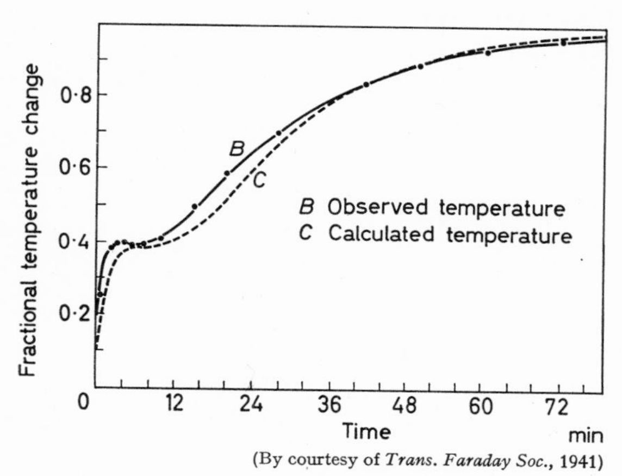

(By courtesy of *Trans. Faraday Soc.*, 1941)

Figure 51. Temperature variation at centre of textile cylinder on passage of moist air (flow experiment)

quantitatively. Its value lies in clarifying the mechanism by which heat and moisture are transferred, in making possible rough estimates of conditioning times, and, in particular, in showing how the times for any given package can be estimated from measurements on a standard package.

REFERENCES

1 A. B. D. Cassie, *J. Text. Inst.*, **31,** T17 (1940).
2 A. B. D. Cassie and S. Baxter, *Trans. Faraday Soc.*, **36,** 458 (1940).
3 P. S. H. Henry, *Proc. Roy. Soc.*, **171A,** 215 (1939).
4 A. B. D. Cassie, *Trans. Faraday Soc.*, **36,** 453 (1940).
5 H. E. Daniels, *Trans. Faraday Soc.*, **37,** 506 (1941).
6 P. S. H. Henry, *Disc. Faraday Soc.*, No. 3, 243 (1948).
7 H. S. Carslaw and J. C. Jaeger, *Conduction of Heat in Solids*, Oxford, 1947.
8 J. Crank, *The Mathematics of Diffusion*, Oxford, 1956.

CHAPTER 9

DIFFUSION IN FIBRE-FORMING SUBSTANCES

By J. Crank

In this chapter we are concerned with the basic process by which water vapour, and organic vapours in general, penetrate fibre-forming substances. The process is essentially one of diffusion which we can describe as 'the process by which matter is transported from one part of a system to another as a result of random molecular motions'. It is the same process as that by which two gases or two solutions mix when brought into contact, but when it takes place in high-polymer substances it becomes a much more complicated process with many new features. The uptake of moisture by a single textile fibre is one practical example of such a diffusion process. Other examples, familiar in textiles, are the removal of solvent from man-made fibres during spinning or extrusion, the corresponding process in the casting of plastic sheet and film, and certain aspects of dyeing.

We have already seen that an attempt to measure the rate of diffusion of water into an individual wool fibre was not successful, because the effect was masked by the large amount of heat evolved and because the diffusion was much faster than the rate at which the heat could get away. In fact, a cooling curve was observed. This heating is a fundamental difficulty in measurements of this kind and different ways of overcoming it have been used; first, Hermans (*1*) studied diffusion into what he called 'model' filaments, which are relatively thick fibres of regenerated cellulose. They are homogeneous and transparent, and have a diameter of about $\frac{1}{2}$ mm, which is some 25 times greater than that of a wool fibre. Because they are so much thicker, they absorb moisture much more slowly, and diffusion, rather than the escape of heat, becomes the rate-controlling process. The heat can escape rapidly enough not to cause any serious rise in temperature. Partly for the same reason, King (*2*) used horn in sheet form to study the diffusion of water vapour, and, since horn is physically and chemically similar to wool, he considered that his results applied to this fibre. Finally, the difficulty can be avoided by choosing vapours which diffuse so slowly that the heat of sorption produces a negligible temperature rise even in a single textile fibre. This is true for ethyl alcohol and wool.

Most measurements of rates of diffusion have been made on a polymer specimen in the form of a plane sheet, because both the experimental arrangements and the interpretation of the results are thereby simplified. Calculations have been made of the temperature change which accompanies the sorption of vapour, on the assumptions that the temperature rises because of the heat of condensation given up at the surface and the heat of mixing is negligible (*3*). An estimate of the temperature change to be expected in an experiment can thus be made.

EXPERIMENTS ON MODEL FIBRES

We shall consider first some of Hermans's results obtained with model filaments of regenerated cellulose. *Figure 52* shows the rate of

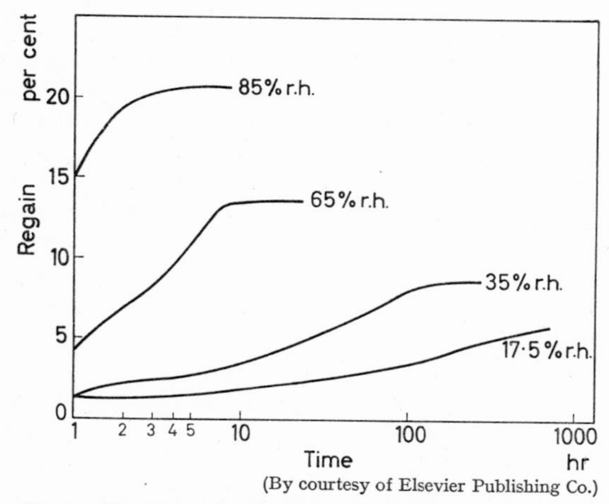

(By courtesy of Elsevier Publishing Co.)

Figure 52. Rate of moisture uptake by model filaments of regenerated cellulose

uptake of moisture by such filaments when exposed to moving air-streams of different humidities. The initial water content of the fibres was about 1%. The differences in conditioning times are so large that it is necessary to use a logarithmic time-scale. The conditioning time is increased by 100-fold if the relative humidity falls from 85% to 17·5%. It is quite clear that diffusion is much slower the lower the moisture content of the fibres.

This is in agreement with the well-known observation that the last stages of removal of moisture from fibres are extremely slow. When most of the moisture has been removed, so that the remaining moisture content is everywhere small, diffusion becomes progressively slower as further moisture is removed and Hermans's results indicate this effect to be very considerable. There is an obvious danger here in connection with the measurement of hysteresis effects. While we have no grounds on which to dispute the existence of genuine hysteresis in fibre–moisture relations, i.e., of different equilibrium uptakes depending on whether the fibre is gaining or losing moisture, it is clear that adequate precautions must be taken to ensure that equilibrium

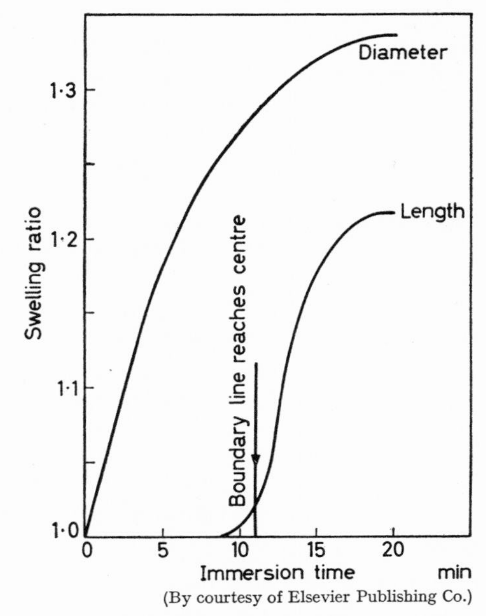

(By courtesy of Elsevier Publishing Co.)

Figure 53. Changes in length and diameter of fibres immersed in water

is truly achieved and that this may involve waiting a very long time when a fibre is losing moisture. It may be necessary to wait several months in some cases.

Hermans (*1*) also measured changes in the length and thickness of a fibre immersed in water. The results for fibres initially bone dry are particularly interesting (*Figure 53*). During the first eight minutes only the thickness increases. After this the length increases rapidly and length and thickness seem to reach their steady values at much the same time. When this experiment was followed under the microscope a sharp boundary line was observed, which moved slowly from the outside of the fibre towards its centre, apparently separating the swollen outer part from the still-dry inner core. When the boundary line had penetrated a certain way, transverse fissures or cracks appeared in the central, dry part of the fibre. The moment at which the boundary reached the centre of the fibre is indicated by the arrow in *Figure 53* and it is at this point that the fibre starts to increase rapidly in length. It seems safe to conclude from these observations that longitudinal swelling of the outside of the fibre is prevented by the mechanical restraint of the core which is still dry (the presence of stresses is indicated by the fissures), but that once the moisture has penetrated to the centre the restraint is removed and the fibre can swell longitudinally as well as radially. Hermans also observed the boundary line in fibres exposed to air of relative humidity as low as 35%. While it is most easily seen in model filaments, Hermans also observed the boundary in a cuprammonium rayon textile fibre. Later, Hartley (*4*) stressed that such an advancing boundary is to be expected as a general phenomenon in any system for which the diffusion rate is much less at low than at high concentrations of the diffusing substance.

MEASUREMENT OF CONCENTRATION-DEPENDENCE

Since Hermans's early observations on the water–cellulose system, it has been realized that a marked dependence of diffusion rate on concentration, such as he observed, is very common in penetrant–polymer systems. This concentration-dependence has been studied in recent years by several workers using different methods. All interpret their results in terms of a diffusion coefficient, D, defined by the relationship

$$\text{Rate of transfer across unit area} = -D\,.\,\mathrm{d}c/\mathrm{d}x$$

where $\mathrm{d}c/\mathrm{d}x$ is the concentration gradient measured along the direction of diffusion. In dilute solutions D is constant, but in the polymer systems with which we are concerned D usually increases as c, the concentration of solvent, is increased, although in some instances it either remains constant or decreases. Techniques for measuring diffusion coefficients fall into one of four categories.

Steady-state permeation method

The polymer film is used as a membrane or diaphragm separating two compartments containing the diffusing vapour. The pressures on the two sides of the membrane are different and are kept essentially constant during the experiment, though a very small change on one side is sometimes used as a measure of the amount of vapour passing through the membrane. By observing the rate of transfer of vapour for different pressures on the high pressure side and a constant (often zero) pressure on the other side, the dependence of diffusion rate on vapour pressure can be deduced. King (*2*), for example, studied the diffusion of water in horn in this way, and a similar method has been used for polythene and nylon (*5*) and for methylene chloride and polystyrene (*6*). Alternative experimental arrangements have been reviewed by Newns (*7*).

Absorption–desorption method

If a sheet of polymer is suspended from a quartz spring in a well-stirred vapour maintained at a constant pressure, the amount of vapour taken up by the sheet can be measured at any time by observing the extension of the spring. A cruder alternative is to remove the sheet from the vapour periodically and weigh it. From a single absorption–time curve a mean diffusion coefficient can be deduced for the conditions of the experiment. Crank and Park (*8*) obtained absorption–time curves for chloroform in polystyrene at a number of different vapour pressures, and from the family of curves deduced the concentration-dependence of diffusion rate. Their method has since been refined and calibration curves are available which make the calculation of a diffusion coefficient from the experimental results straightforward (*3*). When the desorption–time curve is also obtained, the mean of the half-times for absorption and desorption provides a basis for a simpler approximate method of deducing the concentration-dependence (*9, 10*). These absorption and absorption–desorption techniques have been widely used.

Analysis of the concentration distribution

A quite different technique is to observe the concentration distribution during a diffusion experiment. This can be done by the Lamm-scale technique (*11*) in which a uniform scale is viewed through the diffusing medium and the concentration gradient at different points is deduced from the local distortions of the scale. Alternatively, the interferometric technique introduced by Robinson (*12*) can be used. Here the concentration distribution, from which the diffusion coefficient can be calculated, is deduced from the optical interference pattern produced when unidirectional diffusion takes place within a polymer film clamped between silvered plates.

Radioactive-tracer techniques

Isotopic techniques have recently been applied to the measurement of diffusion rates in polymers under conditions of uniform chemical composition (*13, 14*). The importance of tracer techniques is more easily appreciated when some of the complications associated with the interpretation of diffusion experiments carried out in the presence of a gradient of chemical composition are realized. These have been the subject of several papers (*3, 4, 15–17*) which have discussed the mass-flow of the polymer that occurs as the vapour diffuses in (this flow is commonly referred to as the swelling of the polymer) and have handled mathematically the implications of such a flow. The effects of the non-ideality of the system on diffusion rates have also been considered in these papers. These and other difficulties associated with slow changes of polymer structure which may accompany diffusion and which are referred to later are side-stepped by the use of tracers. There are considerable advantages in being able to do this when the aim is to unravel the molecular mechanism by which diffusion occurs. Other methods of measuring diffusion coefficients, however, have a more direct bearing on technological matters such as the rates of conditioning of fibres to given moisture contents.

Because of these complicating features, which appear in some experiments but not in others, different methods of measurement may yield different values for the diffusion coefficient, even in one system. Theoretical relationships have been proposed to relate these different values (*3, 15*). To some extent they must be regarded as tentative until they have been subjected to more experimental verification than has yet been possible.

CHARACTERISTIC GENERAL FEATURES

Above the second-order transition temperature

The general features of diffusion behaviour in polymers are markedly dependent on whether the polymer is above or below its second-order transition temperature. *Figure 54* shows curves plotted against the square root of time for the absorption and desorption of propane by polyisobutene at 35°C, as measured by Prager and Long (*10*). Solutions of the diffusion equation calculated for different types of variable diffusion coefficient (*9, 18*) show that these curves have the characteristic features associated with a diffusion coefficient which depends only on the concentration of the diffusing substance and which increases as concentration is increased. These general features are:

(*a*) Both curves are initially linear, the absorption curve remaining so for over 50% of the final uptake.

(*b*) Above the linear portions both curves are concave towards the (time)$^{\frac{1}{2}}$ axis.

(*c*) Desorption is throughout slower than absorption, the final stages being very slow, as we have already noted.

The general shape, especially of the absorption curve, is very much the same as for a constant diffusion coefficient. In contrast, the

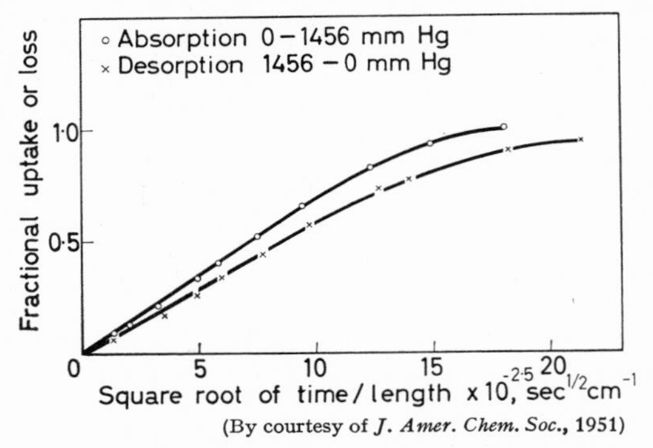

(By courtesy of *J. Amer. Chem. Soc.*, 1951)

Figure 54. Absorption and desorption of propane by polyisobutene at 35°C

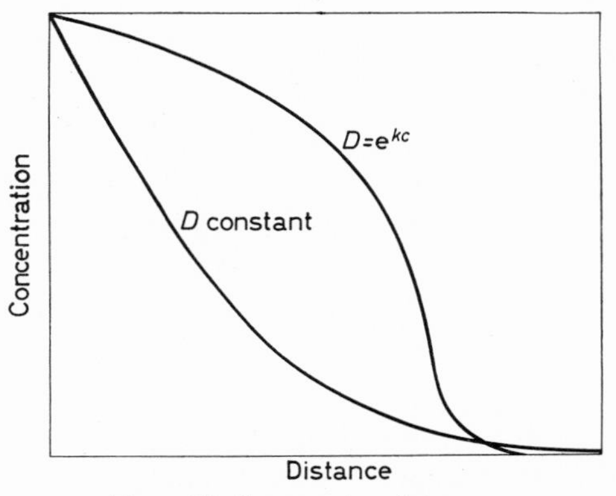

Figure 55. Concentration–distance curves

concentration–distance curve for a diffusion coefficient which increases exponentially with increasing concentration, i.e., $D = e^{kc}$, is quite different from that for a constant diffusion coefficient (*Figure 55*).

Below the second-order transition temperature

The curves of *Figure 56*, which were obtained by Bagley and Long (*19*) for the diffusion of acetone in cellulose acetate at 30°C, i.e., below the second-order transition temperature, are markedly different from those of *Figure 54*. The most striking differences are:

(*a*) Neither of the curves is initially linear; the absorption curve is sigmoid in shape, i.e., it has a point of inflexion.
(*b*) The initial slope for desorption is much greater than for absorption, leading to subsequent intersection of the two curves because the final stages of desorption are slow, as is to be expected if the diffusion coefficient decreases as concentration is decreased.

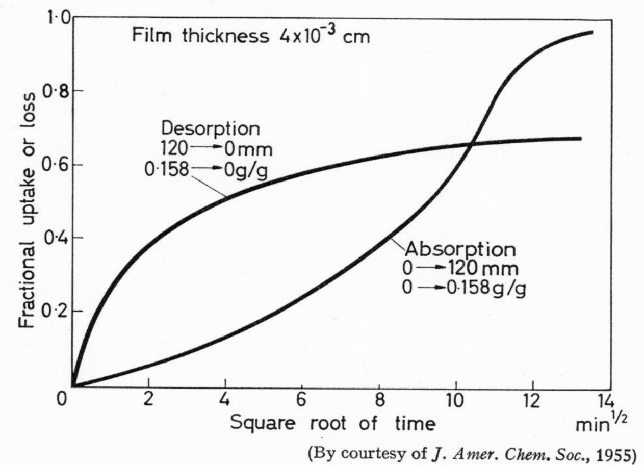

(By courtesy of *J. Amer. Chem. Soc.*, 1955)

Figure 56. Absorption and desorption of acetone by cellulose acetate at 30°C

Now, none of the calculations on concentration-dependent diffusion has ever provided an example of a sigmoid absorption–(time)$^{\frac{1}{2}}$ curve, and we are convinced by the results of these extensive calculations that such a shape is inconsistent with simple concentration-dependence. It has not been possible to prove this by a general argument, although Prager (*20*) has shown rigorously that a point of inflexion cannot occur in the absorption–time (as distinct from (time)$^{\frac{1}{2}}$) curve. Similarly, it is clear from the calculations that no diffusion coefficient which simply increases with concentration, exponentially or in any other way, can cause intersecting absorption and desorption curves. These anomalies show clearly that in many cases the diffusion of a solvent into fibre-forming substances is influenced by other factors in addition to concentration.

Some possible causes of the anomalies have been examined and it appears that they cannot be accounted for solely by the presence of a skin on the fibre or sheet. Most fibres have a skin, the properties of which are different from those of the centre or core of the fibre, and it was reasonable to expect, therefore, that the anomalies might have

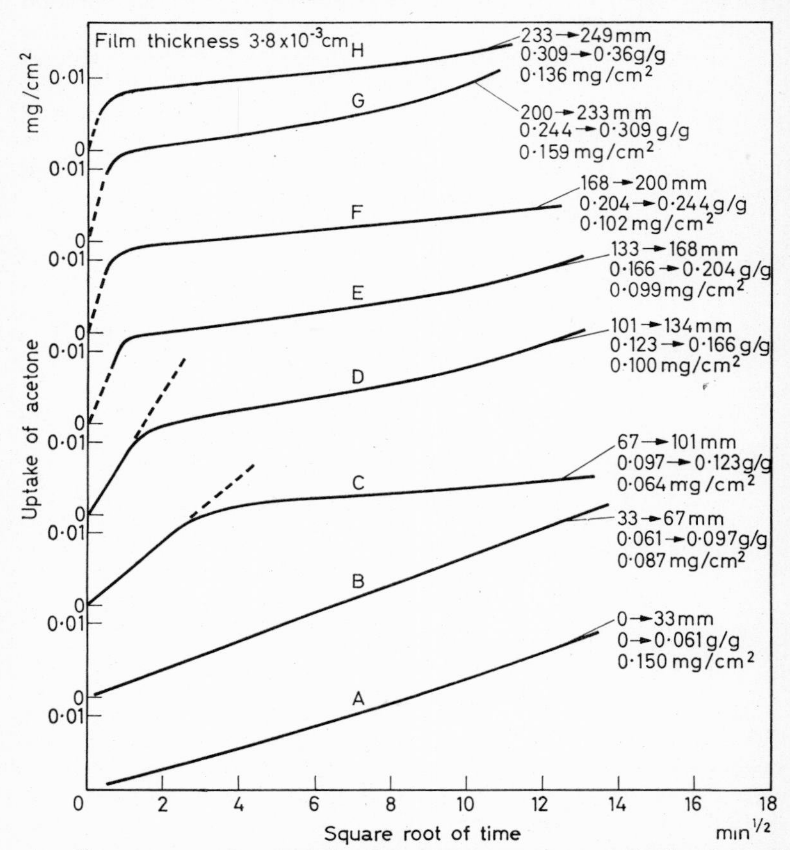

Figures on each curve give the pressure and concentration interval and the equilibrium weight increase

(By courtesy of *J. Amer. Chem. Soc.*, 1955)

Figure 57. Successive interval sorptions of acetone by cellulose acetate at 30°C

been due to such a skin. Crank and Park (*21*) have examined by calculation the diffusion behaviour to be expected from various combinations of skin and core. They chose extreme conditions which seemed most likely to account for the anomalies, and, while it was possible to account for one or two of them separately, they were forced to the conclusion that no type of skin could account for all the anomalous features they had observed. They concluded that the anomalous features are due either to slow changes in polymer structure taking place as diffusion proceeds, or to the internal stresses exerted by one part of the polymer sheet or fibre on another part as it swells. Evidence for such forces is provided by the fissures observed by Hermans and referred to earlier (*1*). These ideas were developed in some detail (*22*, *23*), though neither alone seemed to account for all the observed phenomena.

In the absorption and desorption curves discussed above, the final

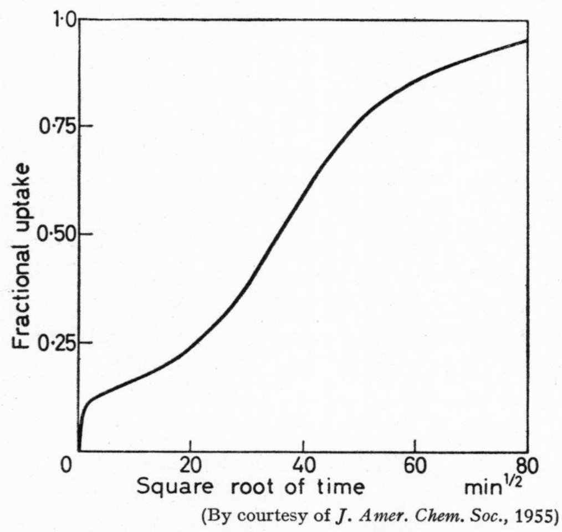

(By courtesy of *J. Amer. Chem. Soc.*, 1955)

Figure 58. Complete absorption curve for Run F of Figure 57

concentration was considerably different from the initial concentration. Subsequently, more information about the behaviour below the second-order temperature has been provided by further experiments of Long and his collaborators (*19*, *24*), who carried out experiments in which the difference between the initial and final concentrations was much smaller. *Figure 57* reproduces the results of some of their experiments carried out over a series of small concentration intervals. The new feature of the curves C to H is that a relatively high rate of sorption, lasting for 1 or 2 minutes and during which 10–15% of the final absorption occurs, is followed by a relatively slow absorption process. A complete absorption curve, as in *Figure 58*, shows that the part corresponding to the slow absorption resembles the absorption curve of *Figure 56*.

Long speaks of 'two-stage sorption' involving a rapid initial stage and a slow second stage. Other evidence presented in his paper reveals that during the first stage acetone penetrates the entire film till a quasi-equilibrium is attained, the sorption being a diffusion-controlled process obeying Fick's law for a concentration-dependent diffusion coefficient. By contrast, the rate in the second stage appears to be controlled, not by diffusion, but by slow changes of polymer structure occurring throughout the sheet in the absence of any concentration gradient (*25*). More generally, the second stage may be controlled jointly by diffusion and polymer relaxation. Two-stage absorption has been observed by Long and his collaborators (*19*) in several systems, by Newns (*26*) in water–cellulose, and by Downes and Mackay (*27*) during the uptake of water by wool. Further thoughts on the nature of two-stage absorption, and desorption, are to be found in the papers referred to.

The detailed mechanism still awaits further study, but by carrying out experiments over small concentration ranges just above and below the second-order temperature, Kokes, Long and Hoard (*28*) seem to have established beyond doubt that this is a critical temperature separating two quite different types of diffusion behaviour. This conclusion is very reasonable in view of other changes in polymer behaviour (*29*) associated with this temperature. Also, it was largely foreshadowed by early observations by Hartley (*30*) who, when studying under the microscope the penetration of methylene chloride and other solvents into cellulose acetate, saw three boundary lines. An inner boundary marked the furthest extent of penetration of the liquid and a second the outer limit of the swollen gel. Between the two Hartley saw a third or 'middle' boundary which, broadly speaking, separated a region of double refraction on the dry side from one of optical isotropy on the highly-swollen side, i.e., separated a region in which the polymer is relaxing very slowly from one in which relaxation is effectively instantaneous. It has yet to be demonstrated conclusively that this boundary occurs at the point where the solvent–polymer mixture has a second-order transition temperature equal to the temperature of the experiment, though this would seem to be a very reasonable conclusion. Hartley also noted that sometimes the inner boundary advanced at a rate proportional to time and not $(\text{time})^{\frac{1}{2}}$ as would be expected on simple diffusion theory. This, too, was an indication of some slow molecular change occurring in the polymer structure.

Diffusion coefficients and their concentration-dependence deduced from sorption experiments below the second-order transition temperature are thus likely to be incorrect unless some allowance is made for these time-dependent factors. With this in mind we shall now examine some factors which control diffusion rates in polymer systems.

FACTORS ON WHICH DIFFUSION RATES DEPEND

Concentration of penetrant

A systematic study of the diffusion of various organic vapours at low concentrations into polyvinyl acetate has been made by Kokes and Long (*31*) at three temperatures, all above the second-order transition temperature. Their results are representative of many others in different systems. They find that the diffusion coefficient as determined from absorption and desorption experiments increases exponentially with increasing vapour concentration; the increase in some cases is as much as 1,000-fold, as the vapour concentration changes from zero to 10% by weight. Concentration-dependence has also been studied systematically for a series of hydrocarbons in polyisobutene (*10*). Hayes and Park (*32*), studying the benzene–rubber system, found much less dependence on concentration, i.e., only a three-fold variation on increasing the benzene concentration by 10%, and their results suggested a linear dependence. Park (*13*) has obtained an exponential dependence for tricresyl phosphate in polystyrene, using a tracer technique. Earlier work (*33–35*) on polystyrene gave similar results, but here the polymer was below its second-order transition temperature. The concentration-dependence has been studied over the whole range of penetrant concentration from zero to fully swollen polymer for polyvinyl acetate (*36*), cellulose acetate (*12*, *37*) and rubber (*38*), using optical techniques.

In contrast to the results obtained with organic vapours, Long and Thompson (*39*) found that the diffusion coefficient for water at 40°C is independent of concentration in polyvinyl acetate, cellulose acetate, cellulose nitrate and nylon 6.10. Furthermore, the diffusion of water nearly obeys Fick's law in these polymers, but with polyvinyl alcohol the anomalous features familiar with organic vapours are to be found. Other work (*40*) suggests the rough generalization that the diffusion of water in markedly water-soluble polymers is always anomalous, but the rate is independent of concentration, or may even decrease with increasing concentration, in polymers that are barely soluble or quite insoluble (*41–43*). On the whole, the diffusion of water is slower in water-soluble than in water-insoluble polymers.

The well-known fact that the presence of water vapour has a marked accelerating effect on the absorption of organic vapours by certain polymers is probably another manifestation of concentration dependence. Long and Thompson (*44*) have confirmed the effect quantitatively for several polymers and have demonstrated that there is little or no effect with polystyrene, which sorbs only small amounts of water. A reasonable explanation is that the small water molecules enter rapidly in advance of the organic vapour and plasticize the polymer, thus making easier the subsequent penetration of vapour. And so we can generalize the statement that the diffusion coefficient for a given vapour increases as the concentration of that vapour is increased, and say that it increases according to the total number of small molecules present in the polymer, regardless of whether they are of the same or different vapours. Desorption, too, is facilitated by the presence of water or other plasticizing molecules, as in the familiar 'water leaching' method of removal of solvent.

The absolute values of the diffusion coefficients vary tremendously for different polymers, being about 10^{-11} cm^2/s for most of the organic vapours in polyvinyl acetate, 10^{-7} cm^2/s in rubber, and 10^{-6} cm^2/s for water in polyvinyl acetate, at zero concentration of vapour and 40°C.

Temperature

Diffusion in polymers proceeds more quickly the higher the temperature and, broadly speaking, the Arrhenius type of equation is obeyed. Kokes and Long (*31*) found that as the molecular size of the penetrant is increased the apparent activation energy, E_a, defined by

$$E_a = -R.\frac{d(\log_e D)}{d(1/T)}$$

first increases and then tends to a limiting value for large molecules. Thus, for water (18 cm^3/mole) the apparent activation energy is 15 kcal, for methanol (41 cm^3/mole) 21 kcal, and for acetone (76 cm^3/mole) 39 kcal, after which there is little change even for a molecule as large as benzene (91 cm^3/mole). The increase in energy with molecular size found with small molecules is to be expected if the 'hole theory' of diffusion is accepted, i.e., if diffusion occurs only when a suitably placed hole appears in the polymer structure large enough for a penetrant molecule to move into it. Kokes and Long (*31*) consider that as the molecular size is increased the activation energy for diffusion should approach that for the viscous flow of the polymer, an idea which is supported by their results on polyvinyl acetate. Apparent activation energies have been obtained in other systems (*32*, *33*). In general, they are higher in polar polymers, such as polyvinyl acetate, than in non-polar polymers, such as polystyrene and polyisobutene. In the benzene–rubber system, Hayes and Park (*32*) found the activation energy to be strongly dependent on temperature, dropping by a factor of three between 0°C and 50°C.

They draw attention to the difficulty of assessing the significance of the mean activation energy when it is temperature-dependent. A similar dependence on temperature has been found by Barrer and Skirrow (*45*) and also by Amerongen (*46*) for small hydrocarbons and simple gas molecules in rubber. The activation energy has also been found to decrease with increasing vapour concentration in several systems, e.g., benzene–rubber (*32*), hydrocarbons in polyisobutene (*47*) and acetone in polyvinyl acetate (*28*).

Molecular volume and shape of penetrant

The value of the diffusion coefficient at a given concentration in a particular polymer depends on the volume and shape of the diffusing

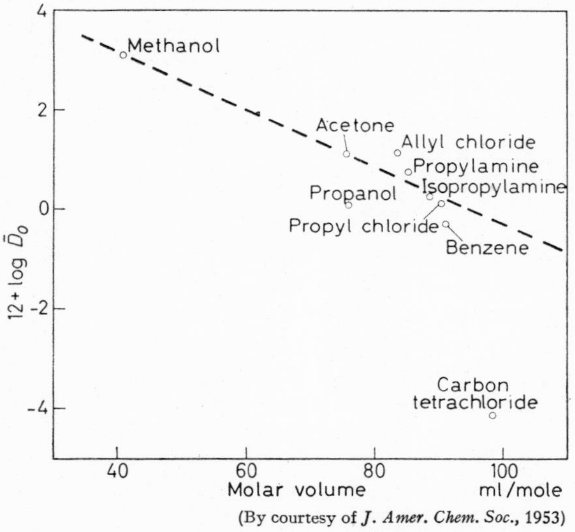

(By courtesy of *J. Amer. Chem. Soc.*, 1953)

Figure 59. Relation between logarithm of diffusion coefficient and molar volume at 40°C

molecule. Roughly speaking, the diffusion coefficient at zero concentration of penetrant decreases exponentially with increasing molecular volume (*10*, *31*, *34*), as would be expected on a 'hole theory' of diffusion (*Figure 59*). Molecular shape, however, has an important modifying influence. A spherical molecule, such as carbon tetrachloride, diffuses much more slowly compared with straight-chain compounds than would be anticipated from its volume alone. Thus, in polyvinyl acetate (*31*), the diffusion coefficient for carbon tetrachloride is roughly one ten-thousandth of those for propylamine and propyl chloride, which are of comparable volume. Prager and Long (*10*), in their study of the diffusion of hydrocarbons into polyisobutene, noted that branching was more important than molecular volume. Park (*34*) reached the same conclusion for various organic vapours in polystyrene, where the diffusion coefficient was found to correlate better with a combination of molecular volume and minimum diameter than with either separately.

Nature of solvent

Kokes and Long (*31*) have examined the effect of the chemical nature of the penetrant, i.e., of the extent to which it is a good or bad solvent. For polyvinyl acetate they find that the diffusion coefficient at zero penetrant concentration does not depend markedly on the nature of the solvent, as measured by the Flory–Huggins parameter. On the other hand, the diffusion rate increases more rapidly with increasing concentration for a poor solvent than it does for a good one. More data are needed before these conclusions can be regarded as generally true.

Nature of polymer

Apart from the polar properties of the polymer, to which we have already referred, there is some evidence that suggests that diffusion rates depend partly on how close the polymer temperature is to its second-order transition temperature. The further above this temperature it is, the greater is the diffusion coefficient for a given penetrant and the less it depends on concentration. Thus, while the diffusion coefficient in polyvinyl acetate, whose transition temperature is 30°C, increases by about 1,000-fold for a change of 10% in penetrant concentration at 35°C, the corresponding variation in rubber (transition temperature −75°C) is only three-fold. For the non-polar polyisobutene, whose transition temperature is close to that of rubber, the variation is 40-fold, which is surprisingly large compared with rubber but much less than that for polyvinyl acetate. Also, Grün (*48*) found that molecular size has a greater influence on diffusion in rubber than in water, but even so the effect in rubber is much less marked than in other polymers.

Hayes and Park (*32*) found that the effect of introducing cross-links into rubber was to decrease the diffusion coefficient and to make it more dependent on the benzene concentration. It was halved in the presence of one cross-link to every 350 carbon atoms in the main hydrocarbon chains.

Orientation of the polymer molecules can have a profound effect on the rates of penetration of small molecules. This was seen by

Hartley (*30*) who observed diffusion into stretched films of cellulose acetate. More information is provided by interferometer photographs (*12*, *37*), which show very clearly that penetration is much slower along the direction of stretch than across it, i.e., it is slower along the direction in which the polymer molecules are preferentially orientated. It appears that the gross effect is due mainly to the considerably reduced capacity for swelling of the polymer along the direction of orientation of the molecules and hence a reduced over-all concentration gradient. The effect on the diffusion coefficient itself is relatively small.

Not only is the rate of penetration influenced by previously induced orientation, but also the degree of orientation is modified by the diffusion process itself. This occurs because the swelling of the sheet tends to orientate the polymer molecules along the direction of diffusion, assuming this to be essentially unidirectional. There is thus a mutual interaction between the orientation and diffusion processes. Evidence for this is provided by direct observation of the birefringence of the polymer during diffusion (*17*) and also by the gradual decrease in sorption rate which is found on successive absorption–desorption cycles (*49*).

In this short review the emphasis has been laid on those features that make diffusion in polymers characteristically different from the diffusion of low-molecular-weight substances in dilute solutions.

ACKNOWLEDGEMENT

It is a pleasure to acknowledge the great help given by my colleague Dr. G. S. Park, who read an early draft of this chapter and made many suggestions for improvement and revision.

REFERENCES

1 P. H. Hermans, *Contribution to the Physics of Cellulose Fibres*, Elsevier, 1946.
2 G. King, *Trans. Faraday Soc.*, **41,** 479 (1945).
3 J. Crank, *The Mathematics of Diffusion*, Oxford, 1956.
4 G. S. Hartley, *Trans. Faraday Soc.*, **42B,** 6 (1946).
5 P. E. Rouse, *J. Amer. Chem. Soc.*, **69,** 1068 (1947).
6 G. S. Park, *Trans. Faraday Soc.*, **48,** 11 (1952).
7 A. C. Newns, *J. Text. Inst.*, **41,** T269 (1950).
8 J. Crank and G. S. Park, *Trans. Faraday Soc.*, **45,** 240 (1949).
9 J. Crank and M. E. Henry, *Trans. Faraday Soc.*, **45,** 636 (1949).
10 S. Prager and F. A. Long, *J. Amer. Chem. Soc.*, **73,** 4072 (1951).
11 T. Svedburg and K. O. Pederson, *The Ultracentrifuge*, Oxford, 1940.
12 C. Robinson, *Proc. Roy. Soc.*, **204A,** 339 (1950).
13 G. S. Park, *Radioisotope Conference*, Oxford, 11 (1954).
14 G. S. Park, *Trans. Faraday Soc.*, **53,** 107 (1957).
15 G. S. Hartley and J. Crank, *Trans. Faraday Soc.*, **45,** 89 (1949).

16 S. Prager, *J. Chem. Phys.*, **21,** 1344 (1953).
17 C. Robinson, *Trans. Faraday Soc.*, **42B**, 12 (1946).
18 J. Crank, *Trans. Faraday Soc.*, **47,** 1 (1951).
19 E. Bagley and F. A. Long, *J. Amer. Chem. Soc.*, **77,** 2172 (1955).
20 S. Prager, private communication.
21 J. Crank and G. S. Park, *Trans. Faraday Soc.*, **47,** 1072 (1951).
22 G. S. Park, *J. Poly Sci.*, **11,** 97 (1953).
23 J. Crank, *J. Poly. Sci.*, **11,** 151 (1953).
24 F. A. Long, E. Bagley and J. Wilkins, *J. Chem. Phys.*, **21,** 1412 (1953).
25 F. A. Long and I. Watts, *J. Poly. Sci.*, **21,** 554 (1956).
26 A. C. Newns, *Trans. Faraday Soc.*, **52,** 1533 (1956).
27 J. G. Downes and B. H. Mackay, *Proc. Int. Wool Text. Res. Conf. Aust.*, 1955, D202.
28 R. J. Kokes, F. A. Long and J. L. Hoard, *J. Chem. Phys.*, **20,** 1711 (1952).
29 R. S. Boyer and R. S. Spencer, *Advances in Colloid Science*, Vol. II, p. 1, Interscience, 1946.
30 G. S. Hartley, *Trans. Faraday Soc.*, **45,** 820 (1949).
31 R. J. Kokes and F. A. Long, *J. Amer. Chem. Soc.*, **75,** 6142 (1953).
32 M. J. Hayes and G. S. Park, *Trans. Faraday Soc.*, **51,** 1134 (1955).
33 G. S. Park, *Trans. Faraday Soc.*, **46,** 684 (1950).
34 G. S. Park, *Trans. Faraday Soc.*, **47,** 1107 (1951).
35 G. S. Park, *Trans. Faraday Soc.*, **48,** 11 (1952).
36 A. T. Hutcheon, R. J. Kokes, R. J. Hoard and F. A. Long, *J. Chem. Phys.*, **20,** 1232 (1952).
37 J. Crank and C. Robinson, *Proc. Roy. Soc.*, **204A,** 549 (1950).
38 M. J. Hayes and G. S. Park, *Trans. Faraday Soc.*, **52,** 949 (1956).
39 F. A. Long and L. J. Thompson, *J. Poly. Sci.*, **15,** 413 (1955).
40 L. J. Hughes and D. B. Fordyce, private communication.
41 R. Taylor, D. Herrmann and A. Kemp, *Industr. Engng Chem.*, **28,** 1255 (1936).
42 F. H. Müller and E. Hellmuth, *Kolloid Zeitschrift*, **144,** 125 (1955).
43 H. Daynes, *Trans. Faraday Soc.*, **33,** 531 (1937).
44 F. A. Long and L. J. Thompson, *J. Poly. Sci.*, **14,** 321 (1954).
45 R. M. Barrer and G. Skirrow, *J. Poly. Sci.*, **3,** 549 (1948).
46 G. J. van Amerongen, *J. Poly. Sci.*, **5,** 307 (1950).
47 S. Prager, E. Bagley and F. A. Long, *J. Amer. Chem. Soc.*, **75,** 1255 (1953).
48 F. Grün, Paper read before American Chemical Society, Chicago, September, 1953.
49 P. Drechsel, J. L. Hoard and F. A. Long, *J. Poly. Sci.*, **10,** 241 (1953).

Chapter 10

MOISTURE AND ELECTRICAL PROPERTIES

By J. W. S. Hearle

In 1729 (*1*), Stephen Grey performed an experiment in which, for the first time, electricity was intentionally conducted from one place to another, from an electrified tube to an ivory ball: the material which he used to conduct the electricity was hempen pack-thread. In order to extend the distance up to 765 ft, he needed to support the thread. When he used fine metal wires for this purpose he found that no electricity reached the ivory ball. However, fine silk filaments proved to be a suitable support. Thus, textile materials provided both the first electric 'cable' and its first insulator. The influence of moisture was soon discovered—by Du Fay, who showed that wet pack-thread was a better conductor. However, in 1734 Grey found that metal wires were better conductors still and interest in the electrical properties of textiles disappeared. It is only in the last thirty years that any detailed work has been done on this subject.

The properties concerned are: dielectric constant, resistance, power factor and static electricity. These will be considered separately.

DIELECTRIC CONSTANT

Figure 60 shows the information on dielectric constant that was available in 1952 for other than dry materials. Dry textiles have a dielectric constant of about 5, and the dielectric constant increases as the material absorbs water. King's (*3*) results for keratin film show the great influence of frequency; and New (*6*) found that the capacity of a condenser containing cotton at 60% relative humidity increased by 50% when the frequency was reduced from 1 Mc/s to 1 kc/s—the change in dielectric constant necessary to cause this depends on the tightness of packing. Because of the variation with frequency, results at a single frequency are not of great value. We can see the effect of orientation in Balls's (*2*) results on cotton fibres.* There are great differences between different materials, cotton and nylon showing a rapid variation of dielectric constant with regain,

* The validity of the extrapolation on which Balls's values were calculated has been questioned in a recent paper (*9*).

while the dielectric constant of wool at a comparable frequency hardly alters.

The value of the dielectric constant depends on the extent to which the material can be polarized, either by the lining up of permanent dipoles or by the formation of induced dipoles. This polarization ranges from the electron distribution in atoms to the distribution of charged ions or even particles. As the frequency increases, the more massive units are unable to follow the rapid changes and cease to contribute to the dielectric constant. Water has a polar molecule—the dielectric constant of pure liquid water at room temperature is

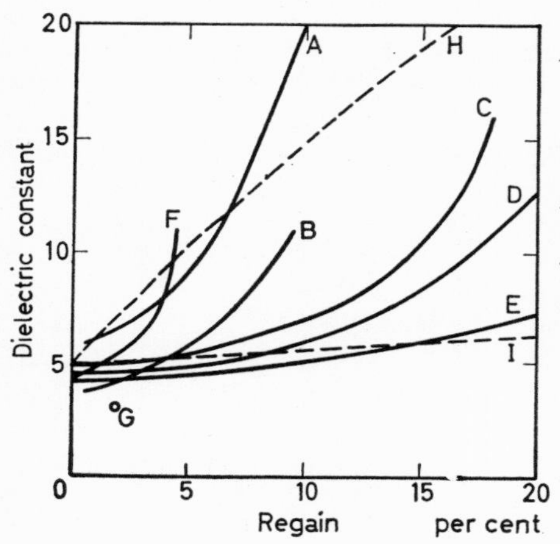

Figure 60. Relation between dielectric constant and regain

Cotton (*2*) 1·75 Mc/s: A–axial; B–transverse.
Keratin film (*3*): C–500 c/s; D–11 kc/s; E–1 Mc/s.
Nylon film: F–11 kc/s (*4*); G–3,000 Mc/s (*5*).
Theoretical: combination of any textile ($\epsilon = 5$) and water ($\epsilon = 81$); H–in parallel; I–in series.

81, below 600 Mc/s—and so its addition to a textile material would be expected to increase the dielectric constant. The magnitude of the increase depends on the arrangement of the materials, and *Figure 60* shows the effective dielectric constant for materials of dielectric constants 5 and 81, arranged in parallel and in series in a condenser; in actual practice the water might be regarded as adding on to, and not displacing, the textile material and this would lead to slightly higher values. But there are other complications. The absorbed water molecules are not free and so may not be able to orientate themselves in the electric field: this will cause a lower dielectric constant than is expected. Argue and Maass (*7*) conclude, as a result of experiments at 20 kc/s, that the effective dielectric constant of the water in purified cotton increases from 16, for that absorbed between 0 and 2% regain, to 70, for that absorbed at regains of between 13 and 15%. On the other hand, the water may, by breaking cross-links, free polar groups in the molecule of the textile material and allow them to line up in the field. At low frequencies there may also be a contribution due to the polarization of the ion distribution: Murphy and Lowry (*8*), in 1930, suggested that this might occur on crystallites in cellulose, and, while this is incompatible with modern views of the structure of cellulose, it may be that there are some closed paths in which the ion distribution can be polarized. If this does happen moisture will have a great effect; at low regains the ions may not be free to move, and at high regains they may move freely through the material, contributing to the conductance, not to the dielectric constant.

TABLE 9

VALUES OF DIELECTRIC CONSTANT (*9, 10*)

Fibre	Frequency (kc/s)	Relative humidity		
		0%	45%	65%
Cotton	1	3·2	7·1	18·0
	100	3·0	4·4	6·0
Viscose rayon	1	3·6	5·4	8·4
	100	3·5	4·7	5·3
Cellulose acetate	1	2·6	3·0	3·5
	100	2·5	2·9	3·3
Wool	1	2·7	3·5	5·5
	100	2·6	3·3	4·6
Ardil	1	2·7	3·2	3·8
	100	2·6	3·0	3·3
Nylon	1	2·5	2·9	3·7
	100	2·4	2·6	2·9
Orlon	1	2·8	3·3	4·2
	100	2·3	2·5	2·8
Dacron	1	2·3	2·3	2·3
	100	2·3	2·3	2·3
Saran	1	2·9	2·9	2·9
	100	2·4	2·4	2·4
Fiberglas	1	3·7	3·7	4·4
	100	3·7	3·7	3·6

Note: These values are extrapolated from results for an air–fibre mixture, and are probably too low. They are nevertheless useful for comparative purposes.

More recent work, summarized in Table 9, suggests that in the cellulosic fibres at higher frequencies the water molecules act as if they were restrained in much the same way as in ice. The polarization, as indicated by the dielectric constant, decreases rapidly in the range between 1 and 100 kc/s. Below 1 kc/s the dielectric constant continues to rise as the frequency is reduced (in contrast to ice, in which it levels off at a value of about 80), and may attain extremely high values at low frequencies and high moisture contents. For example, in cotton at 95% relative humidity and 100 c/s the dielectric constant is over 2,000. This behaviour is probably due to the polarization of the ion distribution, which may alternatively be regarded as a Maxwell–Wagner effect in a non-homogeneous material. It is influenced by the presence of moisture because this frees the ions and allows them to take up a polarized distribution.

In wool the dielectric constant is lower, suggesting that the water molecules are more firmly held, and are not free to orient themselves in the field. This is particularly so at low moisture contents, and supports Speakman's suggestion (*32*) that the moisture first absorbed is firmly bound to hydrophilic groups in the side-chains.

Of fibres which absorb little water, Dacron and Saran show no variation in dielectric constant between 0% and 65% relative humidity. On the other hand, Vinyon and Fiberglas show a considerable increase in dielectric constant at low frequencies as the humidity increases. This is presumably due to surface effects.

RESISTANCE

Moisture is the most important factor in determining the resistance of textile materials: by varying the amount of moisture the resistance may be changed by at least 10^{10} times, and even when the range is restricted to, say, 30 to 90% relative humidity it varies by 100,000 times. The differences between different textiles with the same moisture content also cover a range of about 100,000 times; the effect of reasonable changes in other factors is less.

As is usual with textile materials, it is more convenient to work in terms of mass per unit length, rather than area of cross-section. The mass specific resistance can be defined as the resistance in ohms between the ends of a specimen 1 cm long and of mass 1 g; it is denoted here by R_S. A series of papers published recently (*11–13*) gives considerable experimental information.

The graphs in *Figures 61 and 62* give approximate values of $\log R_S$ plotted against $\log M$, where M is the percentage moisture content, and against the relative humidity. The results of different tests differ widely according to the purity of the material and the particular experimental conditions. A range of about ± 1 in $\log R_S$ should be allowed for these differences. The slopes of the lines remain almost the same.

Various empirical relations have been proposed relating resistance to moisture condition. One of the first was that of Murphy and Walker (*14*) for cotton:

$$\log R = -0{\cdot}085H + A$$

where H is the relative humidity (per cent) and A is a constant the value of which depends on the sample, the electrode system, and whether the specimen is absorbing or desorbing.

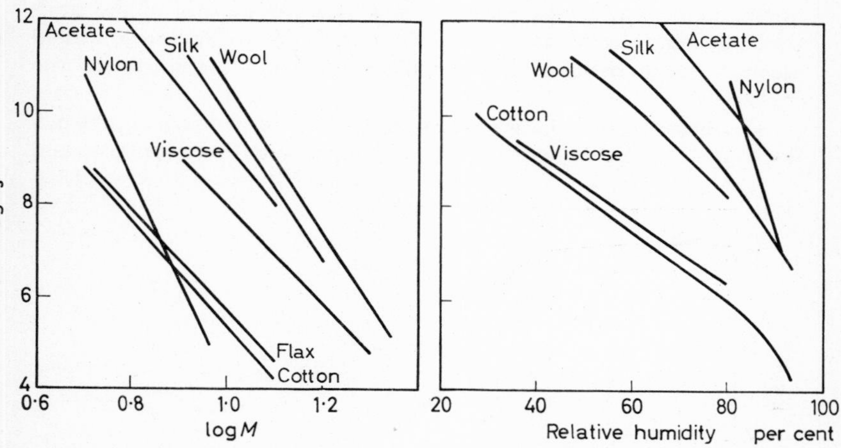

Figure 61. Relation between logarithm of mass specific resistance and percentage moisture content (11)

Figure 62. Relation between logarithm of mass specific resistance and relative humidity (11)

Relations of this form do hold widely, but they have the disadvantage of varying with the position on the hysteresis loop. Later, Walker (*15*) put forward the relations:

$$\log R = ar + b \quad \text{for } r < 3$$
$$\log R = -a' \log r + b' \quad \text{for } 3 < r < 10$$
$$\log R = -a'' H + b'' \quad \text{for } 10 < r < \text{saturation value}$$

where a, a', a'' and b, b', b'' are constants, and r = regain (per cent). Unfortunately, he called r the moisture content, and most later workers have used the relation:

$$\log R_S = -n \log M + \log K,$$

or

$$R_S M^n = K$$

where n and K are constants.

For medium values of M, it makes little difference which relation is used (*21*), though the values of the constants are different. The latter relation is considered here. It is a good approximation for most textile materials for the range of humidities commonly encountered. The value of n for cellulosic materials is about 11, and for protein fibres about 16. There are, however, differences between the results of different experimenters; and, while some of these differences may be due to experimental error, there are probably some real variations due to the different conditions of the experiments. In particular, there seems to be a difference according to the orientation of the fibre between the electrodes. The values of $\log K$ differ more widely according to the material, its purity, and the conditions of the test.

There are some deviations from the simple linear relation between $\log R_S$ and $\log M$. When taken over a wider range the relation is seen

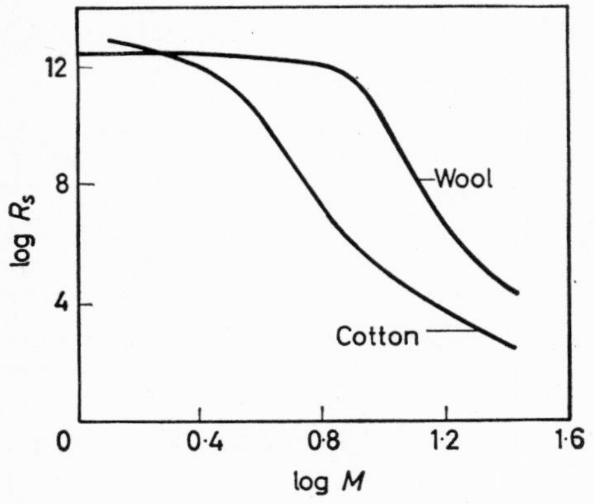

Figure 63. Logarithmic plot of mass specific resistance against percentage moisture content (11)

to be sigmoidal (*Figure 63*). The flattening of the curve at low moisture contents is particularly marked in the protein fibres: for a particular specimen of wool the value of $\log R_S$ was still about 12·3 after standing over anhydrous phosphorus pentoxide for three weeks. For silk the linear portion of the curve is hardly present, there being a definite, though slight, sigmoidal shape even for a range of $\log M$ of 0·9–1·3.

The newer non-hygroscopic textile materials also show a marked variation of resistance with relative humidity; this is probably due to surface conduction. Their values of resistance are very much influenced by the presence of surface finishes.

The moisture content of the material also affects other associated properties. Thus, the back electromotive forces which develop in the material tend to become larger, though more rapidly dissipated, the damper the material; and the variation of resistance with duration of application of voltage is also greater for damp specimens. The resistance is also prone to increase with time at low moisture contents; this is probably due to electrostatic polarization. The rate of decrease of resistance with temperature is less at higher moisture contents, though the extent of the change is different for different materials.

Theories of resistance

Baxter (*16*) has suggested that conduction in wool is by electrons, the water molecules acting as impurity centres in a semi-conductor. But there is much evidence that conduction in textile materials is principally by ions: the products of electrolysis have been observed in experiments on cellulose film and on keratin film; the resistance of textile materials is lowered by increasing the electrolyte content; and effects, such as polarization and back electromotive forces, which are characteristic of electrolytic conduction, have been observed. It thus seems unlikely that electrons are contributing appreciably to the conduction, except possibly in exceptional circumstances.

There are two main lines of thought in the theories that have been put forward to explain the variation of resistance with moisture content. The variation may be due either to a change in the ease with which ions can pass through the material under the influence of the applied field, or to a change in the number of ions available for conduction, due to a change in the degree of dissociation.

As a result of experiments on cellulose film, and particularly on the variation of resistance with temperature, O'Sullivan (*17*) concluded that at high moisture contents—greater than 50% in cellulose film—the conduction is limited by the viscous drag on the ions moving along continuous water paths: as the moisture content increases the diameters of the paths will increase, and so the viscous drag will decrease. At low moisture contents—less than 20% in cellulose film—he supposes that the water paths will be broken; but, since the equilibrium is kinetic, and water molecules are continually evaporating and condensing, the positions of the breaks will be continually changing. Ions will be held up at the breaks until a water molecule condenses and closes the gap. The temperature coefficient of resistance on this theory should be the same as the temperature coefficient of the number of water molecule impacts per second; O'Sullivan's experiments show that this is so. At intermediate moisture contents it is assumed that there is a gradual transition from one mechanism to the other.

O'Sullivan does not attempt to explain quantitatively the effect of moisture content on resistance. Hearle (*18*) has shown that difficulties arise when this is attempted for O'Sullivan's low moisture content theory. The current is given by the expression:

$$I = nqV$$

where n is the number of ions per unit length of specimen, q is the charge on an ion, and V is the mean velocity of the ions, including the stops.

If we assume that the movement along the paths is rapid, so that the only delay is at the breaks, we have:

$$V = 1/Nt$$

where N is the number of breaks per unit length of path and t is the mean time for which an ion is delayed at a break.

There may, however, be some mutual interference of ions at a break, and introducing a factor, f, to correct for this, we get:

$$I = f\frac{nq}{Nt}$$

Therefore, if the applied voltage is E, the resistance, R, is given by:

$$R = \frac{E}{I} = \frac{E}{nq}\frac{Nt}{f}$$

The first difficulty is now obvious: on the simple theory, neglecting the effect of f, the resistance is proportional to the voltage. This happens because the current is saturated, the delays being independent of the applied voltage. In fact, experiment shows that the resistance decreases slightly as the voltage increases.

The main influence of moisture on resistance, on this theory, must come from changes in N, since it can be shown that the change in t, due to a change in the rate of water impacts as the humidity increases, can only cause $\log R$ to decrease by $1{\cdot}4$ as the relative humidity changes from 4 to 100%. The total change in $\log R$ is at least 8.

To obtain a sufficiently large change in N as the moisture content varies, it is necessary to assume, for conduction in a cellulosic material, that a break occurs when about 12 adjacent hydroxyl groups are all free from absorbed water molecules. These groups may be thought of as attached to cellulose molecules surrounding a conduction path. Under these conditions reasonable agreement with the actual variation of resistance with moisture content can be obtained. In order to calculate the number of breaks at a given moisture content, the number of vacant absorption sites can be obtained from Peirce's theory (*33*) of the proportions of water directly and indirectly absorbed; from this the probability of a given number of adjacent groups being free can be calculated.

There is still the difficulty of the factor f. If the ions move along paths to the breaks, positive ions in one direction and negative in the other, then the distribution of ions will be polarized and an electric field opposing the applied field will be set up. If the ion movement necessary for this field to equal the applied field is calculated, it becomes clear that only a small proportion of the total number of ions could move to the breaks in the paths without the reverse field exceeding the applied field. Therefore the factor, f, has a very large effect. Simple attempts to estimate its value, such as equating it to the fraction of ions free to move to a break, lead to expressions of the form:

$$f \propto \frac{EN}{nq}$$

Substitution of this in the expression for R eliminates, among other things, N: and so the variation of N with moisture content would cease to play a part in determining the resistance. However, under conditions in which the movement to breaks is limited by polarization, it seems unlikely that the simple expression for the current would still be a good approximation. It is possible that a proper theory of the movement of ions, limited by breaks and by polarization, would lead to a result in which the variations of N could explain the variation of resistance with moisture content.

The alternative argument considers the number of ions available for conduction. The degree of dissociation into free ions is much affected by the dielectric constant in solvents of low dielectric constant. In applying this idea to textile materials it is difficult to know which is the correct value of dielectric constant to use. There is a choice between the widely different values at different frequencies and for different orientations. Also, the measurements of dielectric constant are made on bulk material, but in considering the forces between ions it may be necessary to take account of local variations of dielectric constant—the ions are likely to be nearer to the absorbed water molecules than they would be if they were distributed at random throughout the material, and so the effective dielectric constant may be higher.

King and Medley (*19*), working on the basis of Bjerrum's theory of ionic dissociation (*34*), have obtained reasonable agreement between experimental measurements of resistance and dielectric constant for keratin and nylon films. However, in view of the doubt about the dielectric constant, a simpler, though cruder, approach has been proposed by Hearle (*18*). It can be shown (*35*), as a result of the law of mass action, that:

$$\frac{\alpha^2}{1-\alpha} = \frac{A'}{n'} e^{-U/kT}$$

where α is the degree of dissociation into free ions, A' is practically constant, n' is the total number of the dissociating molecules per unit volume, U is the energy needed to separate the ions, k is Boltzmann's constant, and T is the absolute temperature.

We may consider the separation of the ions as the separation of two unlike charges in a medium of dielectric constant ϵ. We then have, as a result of Coulomb's law, $U = U_0/\epsilon$, where U_0 is the energy needed to separate the charges in a vacuum. For $\epsilon < 20$, there is evidence that it is reasonable to assume that $\alpha \ll 1$, and therefore:

$$\frac{\alpha^2}{1-\alpha} \simeq \alpha^2$$

and

$$\alpha = \sqrt{\left(\frac{A'}{n'}\right)} e^{-U_0/2\epsilon kT}$$

But the resistance is inversely proportional to the number of free ions, i.e., to the degree of dissociation. Therefore:

$$\begin{aligned} \log R &= \text{constant} - \log \alpha \\ &= \text{constant} + \frac{U_0 \log e}{2kT} \cdot \frac{1}{\epsilon} \\ &= \frac{a}{\epsilon} + b \end{aligned}$$

where a and b are constants.

Application of this expression to Balls's results (*2*) for the dielectric constant of cotton leads to reasonable agreement with experimental values of resistance, as is shown in *Figure 64*. The value of U_0 corresponding to the value used for a is $14 \cdot 8 \times 10^{-12}$ ergs, compared to 5×10^{-12} ergs for the energy of separation of two electronic charges, initially 4×10^{-8} cm apart—this distance is of the order of magnitude of ionic diameters. Good agreement, up to somewhat higher moisture contents, is also obtained between resistance values for wool and King's values (*13*) of the dielectric constant of keratin film. The lower dielectric constant of keratin film, compared to cotton under similar conditions, may explain the higher resistance of protein fibres. If bivalent ions are present instead of monovalent ions, there would be a large increase in U_0, which would explain the very low conductivity found experimentally. Additional direct experimental evidence has been given recently (*20*).

Considering the theoretical position generally, we may say that the variation of dielectric constant offers a reasonable explanation of many of the phenomena, provided that the effective dielectric constant is similar to the measured bulk dielectric constant. Alternatively, it is possible that variations in the number of breaks in conducting paths could be the explanation, though there are serious difficulties in the simple theory. In either case a closer study of the nature of the movement of ions in the material is needed. At high

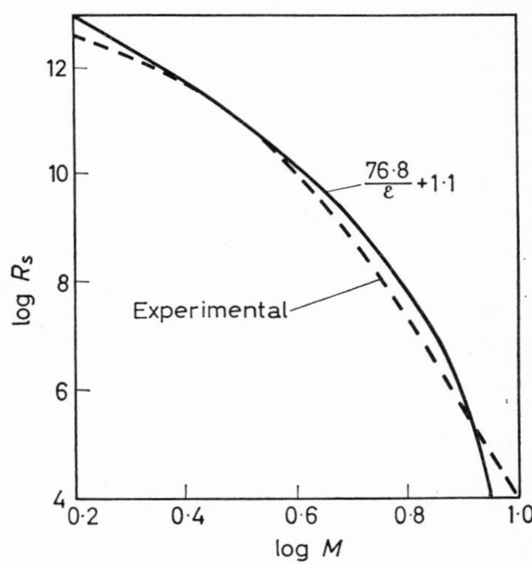

Figure 64. Comparison of experimental and theoretical relationships between mass specific resistance and percentage moisture content (*18*)

moisture contents, when dissociation is almost complete, and when the number of breaks is negligible, the limiting factor is probably the viscous hindrance of ions.

POWER FACTOR AND A.C. RESISTANCE

Power factor is defined as the ratio of energy loss in a condenser to the product of voltage and current. If we imagine the condenser as a capacitance, C, in parallel with a resistance, R, then the power factor is $1/\omega CR$, if $R \gg 1/\omega C$, where $\omega/2\pi$ is the frequency. The power factor is therefore closely related to the A.C. resistance and to the dielectric constant.

New (*16*) has measured the power factor of several textile materials at an arbitrary degree of packing (*Figures 65 and 66*). The great effect of humidity and of frequency can be seen. The effect of frequency depends on the humidity; and at medium humidities a plot of power factor against frequency shows a minimum, which shifts to higher frequencies at higher humidities. New concludes, and this is sup-

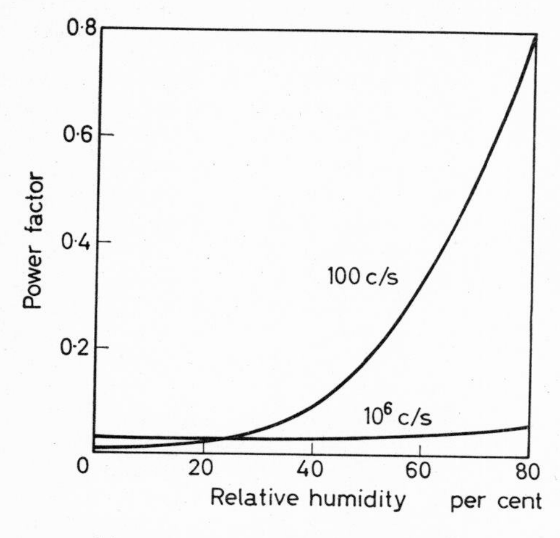

Figure 65. Relation between power factor and relative humidity for cotton (arbitrary packing) (16)

ported by some experiments of Murphy (*22*), that at high humidities and low frequencies the results are explained by the effect of the D.C. resistance, but that at lower humidities and at higher frequencies other factors must be involved.

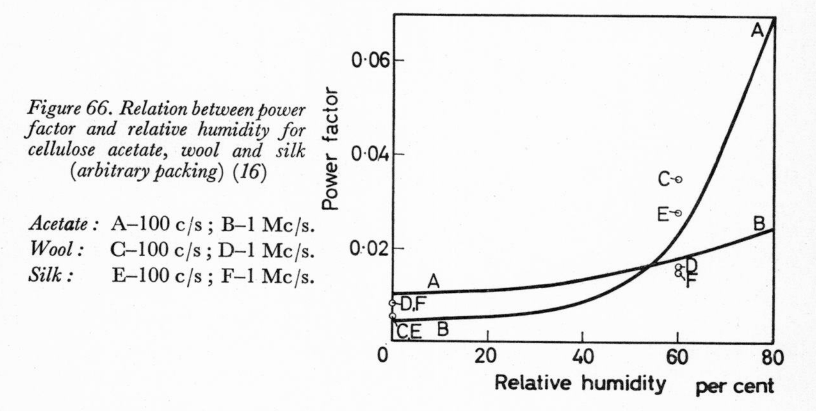

Figure 66. Relation between power factor and relative humidity for cellulose acetate, wool and silk (arbitrary packing) (16)

Acetate : A–100 c/s ; B–1 Mc/s.
Wool : C–100 c/s ; D–1 Mc/s.
Silk : E–100 c/s ; F–1 Mc/s.

More recent results (*9*, *10*) are given in Table 10. The rise at low frequencies, which in cotton at high humidities shows a maximum at about 100 c/s, is connected with the relaxation effects occurring in the orientation of the absorbed water molecules, and, at lower frequencies, of the ion distribution. Because of a variety of effects spreading over a range of frequencies, the maximum found in the power factor at between 10 and 100 kc/s is not observed. There is also an indication, as a result of work at lower and higher frequencies, of a maximum in the power factor between 10 and 100 Mc/s, which is a region not easily amenable to experiment. The tests at below 10 Mc/s suggest that this maximum is not much affected by the presence of moisture.

TABLE 10

VALUES OF POWER FACTOR FOR YARNS WOUND BETWEEN CONES AT A PACKING DENSITY OF ABOUT 50% (*9*, *10*)

Fibre	Frequency (kc/s)	Relative humidity		
		0%	45%	65%
Cotton	1	0·015	0·25	0·63
	100	0·015	0·08	0·16
Viscose rayon	1	0·007	0·08	0·40
	100	0·015	0·02	0·03
Cellulose acetate	1	0·006	0·008	0·020
	100	0·006	0·009	0·013
Wool	1	0·01	0·04	0·12
	100	0·01	0·02	0·04
Ardil	1	0·01	0·03	0·08
	100	0·01	0·015	0·02
Nylon	1	0·01	0·025	0·06
	100	0·02	0·03	0·055
Orlon	1	0·02	0·025	0·04
	100	0·008	0·015	0·02
Dacron	1	0·002	0·005	0·007
	100	0·004	0·009	0·012
Saran	1	0·05	0·055	0·06
	100	0·04	0·04	0·04
Fiberglas	1	0·002	0·105	0·15
	100	0·002	0·005	0·01

It is of importance in high-frequency drying that the power factor should increase with humidity, for it means that the most heat is generated in the dampest places, so that the process tends to maintain uniform drying.

STATIC ELECTRICITY

It has been suggested by Keggin, Morris and Yuill (*23*) that the amount of static charge generated in any process is independent of the nature of the fibre or its moisture content. While this may not prove to be exactly true, it is probably a good approximation. It is supported by Medley's view (*24*) that the charge generated on separating two insulators is limited by the conductivity of the air. If Q_0 is the charge generated, the charge Q_r at a later time is given by:

$$Q_r = Q_0 - Q_e$$

where Q_e is the amount of charge that has leaked away.

The leakage will be greater the lower the resistance. Thus the resistance, and hence the moisture content, has a great effect on the

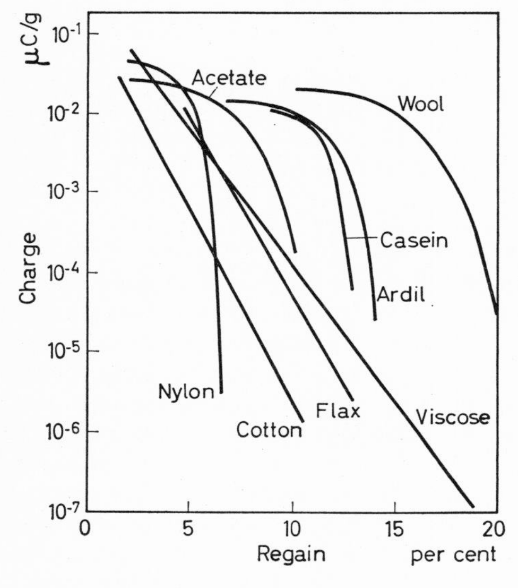

Figure 67. Relation between static charge and relative humidity (*23*)

residual charge, Q_r. *Figure 67* shows values of Q_r, obtained by Keggin *et al.*, after the carding of staple fibres. It will be seen that the charge tends to a constant value at low regains, when Q_e is neglible; that the charge decreases as the regain increases; and that the low-resistance fibres show the smallest charge. At 65% relative humidity, the charge varied from the maximum of about 0·02 micro-coulombs per gram for nylon, cellulose acetate, and wool, to about 10^{-5} for cotton and viscose rayon. The point at which the materials became difficult to handle depended on other properties of the fibres as well as on the charge present.

More recent measurements (*25–27*) on a variety of systems, e.g., rovings and cloth passing through rollers, and films and filaments passing over platinum strips, have confirmed the general form of curve shown in *Figure 67.* At low humidities the static charge is constant (or may rise slightly as the humidity is increased), but, when a certain critical humidity is passed, the magnitude of the charge observed falls rapidly for any further increase in humidity. Similar effects are found when the conductivity of the material is changed by any other method.

Medley has shown that the critical conductivity for reduction of charge occurs when the flow of current back through the material becomes comparable with the rate at which the charge is carried forward by the material. He has worked out and confirmed experimentally a relation between critical conductivity and the speed of the material.

When the conductivity of the material is less than the critical value, the charge carried forward on the material is limited by the leakage through the air near the point of separation; its magnitude is therefore determined by the properties of the air and the geometry of the system.

MEASUREMENT OF MOISTURE ELECTRICALLY

All the properties described have been used as a measure of the moisture condition of textiles. The experimental methods are all arbitrary and have to be calibrated by a gravimetric method. They have, however, numerous advantages: as laboratory instruments they provide a rapid, easy, often direct-reading, and usually non-destructive test of regain; the variation of regain over a specimen can frequently be obtained; and the instruments are usually portable, so that they can be used on material anywhere in the mill. As process control instruments they provide a continuous indication of moisture condition and may provide automatic control. Even if the indication of moisture is only arbitrary, as in the Shirley Electrical Hygrometer when used on the stenter, they allow the management to specify a condition that can be maintained, and to investigate the effect of changing the condition in a way that could not be done when the moisture condition was determined by the feel of the material.

The onset of static is used as an indication of moisture condition in the Dritester instrument. The claim was made that this corresponds to the 'natural moisture condition' of the material, but the experimental results show that it does not correspond to a given humidity. For material with a low resistance, such as cotton, static electricity would not appear in any quantity until the material was much drier than it need be. In general, static is not likely to be a good indicator of moisture content.

Power factor has been tried, but does not appear to have been used in a commercial instrument for the measurement of moisture in textiles.

The most-used methods rely on the measurement of dielectric constant or resistance. Resistance has the inherent advantage of a much more rapid variation with moisture condition. Thus, a change in regain from 5% to 10% decreases the resistance of cotton 1,000 times, but the dielectric constant is little more than doubled; for wool the contrast is greater still. This means that the effect of any other sources of error, such as variation in dimensions, is much greater in a capacitance method; indeed, the variation in capacity can be used to measure irregularity. As laboratory instruments, capacitance meters also possess the defect of requiring a given weight of material between the plates of the condenser—for textile materials the only way to obtain this is to weigh the material, which makes the test less convenient. For resistance meters this difficulty can be overcome, as in the Shirley Moisture Meter, by using an electrode system which is pressed on to the material. Resistance methods are limited in that they may not be able to deal with fibres of very high resistance, because of difficulties of measurement, insulation, and consistency.

The principal British laboratory instrument is the Shirley Moisture Meter (*28*), a resistance meter; and the principal process-control instruments are the Shirley Hygrometer, using resistance, and the Fielden Drimeter (*29*), using capacity. There are also a number of American and other instruments (*30*). The Shirley instruments, designed by E. H. Jones, are easily adjusted; accurate—in tests on the Moisture Meter with a number of types of cotton, 84% of the readings showed a difference from oven tests of less than 0·3% in the value of the regain; and sensitive—the scale divisions, about 1/50th of the indicator movement, are of 0·1% regain on the Moisture Meter; and they cover a reasonably wide range—5 to 15% in regain for cotton. Different calibrations are needed for materials other than raw cotton and grey cotton yarn; and the Moisture Meter is unsatisfactory for use on materials of very high resistance.

The Fielden Drimeter has the disadvantage of requiring the passage of dry material during the preliminary adjustment, which is an inconvenience and may be a source of error if the material is not really dry. The instrument is not very sensitive—the usual range covered is 0 to 20% regain on half the total indicator movement, which does not allow for as fine a control of the machine as is desirable. Different calibrations are needed for different materials. The meter reading is much affected by any puckering of the material, possibly due to the higher longitudinal dielectric constant.

In general with instruments of this sort it is essential either to ensure that the calibration has been thoroughly checked on material similar to that for which it is being used or to check the instrument by comparison with oven tests. There is no doubt that, for the purposes for which they are recommended, the Shirley instruments have been thoroughly tested, and for these purposes they are probably the best instruments available.

REFERENCES

Historical

1 J. Priestly, *A Familiar Introduction to the Study of Electricity*, Vol. 1, 3rd ed., p. 36 *et seq.*, London, 1777.

Dielectric constant

2 W. L. Balls, *Nature*, **158,** 9 (1946).
3 G. King, *Trans. Faraday Soc.*, **43,** 601 (1947).
4 G. King, *J. Colloid Sci.*, **2,** 551 (1947).
5 T. M. Shaw and J. J. Windle, *J. Appl. Phys.*, **21,** 956 (1950).
6 A. A. New, *Electrical Communication*, **19,** 71 (1940).
7 G. H. Argue and O. Maass, *Canad. J. Res.*, **B13,** 156 (1935).
8 E. J. Murphy and E. H. Lowry, *J. Phys. Chem.*, **34,** 598 (1930).
9 J. W. S. Hearle, *Text. Res. J.*, **24,** 307 (1954).
10 J. W. S. Hearle, *Text. Res. J.*, **26,** 108 (1956).

Resistance

11 J. W. S. Hearle, *J. Text. Inst.*, **44,** T117 (1953).
12 G. E. Cusick and J. W. S. Hearle, *J. Text. Inst.*, **46,** T369 (1955).
13 G. E. Cusick and J. W. S. Hearle, *J. Text. Inst.*, **46,** T699 (1955).
14 E. J. Murphy and A. C. Walker, *J. Phys. Chem.*, **32,** 1761 (1928).
15 A. C. Walker, *J. Text. Inst.*, **24,** T123 (1933).
16 S. Baxter, *Trans. Faraday Soc.*, **39,** 207 (1943).
17 J. B. O'Sullivan, *J. Text. Inst.*, **39,** T368 (1948).
18 J. W. S. Hearle, *J. Text. Inst.*, **44,** T177 (1953).
19 G. King and J. A. Medley, *J. Colloid Sci.*, **4,** 9 (1949).
20 J. W. S. Hearle, *J. Text. Inst.*, **48,** T40 (1957).

The earlier literature is reviewed in:

21 J. W. S. Hearle, *J. Text. Inst.*, **43,** P194 (1952).

Power factor

22 E. J. Murphy, *J. Phys. Chem.*, **33,** 200 (1929).

Static electricity

23 J. F. Keggin, G. Morris and A. M. Yuill, *J. Text. Inst.*, **40,** T702 (1949).
24 J. A. Medley, *Nature*, **166,** 524 (1950).
25 V. E. Gonsalves and B. J. van Dongeren, *Text. Res. J.*, **24,** 1 (1954).
26 J. A. Medley, *J. Text. Inst.*, **45,** T123 (1954).
27 J. A. Medley, *Brit. J. Appl. Phys.*, Suppl. No. 2, 523 (1953).

Static electricity—cont.

28 E. H. Jones, *J. Sci. Instrum.*, **17,** 55 (1940).
29 Fielden (Electronics) Ltd., *Electronic Engng*, **21,** 10 (1949).
30 R. K. Toner, C. F. Bowen and J. C. Whitwell, *Text. Res. J.*, **18,** 526 (1948); **19,** 1 (1949); **19,** 755 (1949); **20,** 400 (1950).
31 Anon., *The Shirley Moisture Meter*, Record Electrical Co. Ltd., Altrincham, 1949.

Miscellaneous

32 J. B. Speakman, *Trans. Faraday Soc.*, **40,** 6 (1944).
33 F. T. Peirce, *J. Text. Inst.*, **20,** T133 (1929).
34 N. K. Bjerrum, *Danske Vidensk. Selsk., Mat.-fys. Medd.*, **9,** 2 (1926).
35 J. Frenkel, *Kinetic Theory of Liquids*, p. 432, Oxford, 1946.

CHAPTER 11

EFFECT OF MOISTURE ON DENSITY AND OPTICAL PROPERTIES

By R. Meredith

This chapter is concerned with the effect of moisture on the density and on the optical properties of fibres. It is necessary first to clarify our ideas of what is meant by density when the term is applied to a porous substance such as a fibre. Accordingly, the concept of density is first discussed before describing the relation between moisture and density. The effect of moisture on the optical properties of cellulose fibres can be interpreted in a manner which fits in with the effect of moisture on density. As far as the interpretation of the results is concerned, by far the greatest amount of information available relates to cellulose fibres. Hence, much of what follows is concerned with cellulose, although the picture built up might be applied to other fibres if the necessary modification of details were made.

THE CONCEPT OF DENSITY OF FIBRES

The determination of the density or mass per unit volume of a substance requires the evaluation of the mass and volume of a given sample of the material. The mass of a sample of textile fibres is relatively easily measured, but the determination of the volume presents a difficult problem. There is considerable evidence to show that textile fibres contain pores which may range in size from molecular dimensions up to minute cracks visible under the optical microscope. When such fibres are immersed in a wetting but non-swelling fluid by some method which excludes traces of moisture and air, the fibre pores are filled with the fluid to an extent depending on the size of the fluid molecules and the accessibility of the internal space to the outer atmosphere. It will be seen that the problem in determining the volume of a fibre reduces to one of deciding how much pore space is to be regarded as inside, and how much outside, the fibre substance.

Fluids available for measuring the volume of fibres are gases such as hydrogen, helium and oxygen, and liquids such as benzene, toluene, carbon tetrachloride, mercury and water. Not all of these are suitable for measuring the volume of the fibre substance for various reasons. Some of the gases, e.g., hydrogen and oxygen, may be adsorbed by the fibre, mercury does not wet the fibre and water swells most fibres. Nevertheless, the measurement of density in each of these fluids helps to build up a concept of the true density of a fibrous material.

TABLE 11

DENSITY OF CELLULOSIC FIBRES

Fibre	Density (g/cm³)			
	in helium	in toluene	in water	from X-rays
Native cotton, American	1·567	1·550	1·610	1·591
Mercerized cotton, American	1·550	1·536	1·607	1·589
Cuprammonium rayon	1·531	1·522	1·601	1·589

The densities of dry cellulose fibres, measured in helium, in toluene and in water by Davidson (*1*), are recorded in Table 11. These results show that the density of each fibre in helium is slightly greater than in toluene, whilst the density in water is much higher than in either of the non-swelling fluids. As a reference value, the density of crystalline cellulose deduced from X-ray measurements is included in the table and it will be noticed that the density of cotton and rayon in non-swelling fluids is less than the density of crystalline cellulose; the density in water is greater than that of crystalline cellulose. The data suggest that helium and toluene do not penetrate completely the pores in the amorphous regions and that water is compressed when it enters and swells the cellulose fibres.

Different workers hold various opinions as to the 'true' density of cellulose in its fibrous form. Thus, Davidson (*1*) and Stamm (*2*) suggest that the density in helium is the true density and that the water absorbed by the cellulose is compressed. Lauer (*3*) suggests that the density in water is the true density. This is a view which was supported by Hermans (*4*). Thus, here we have two different opinions as to what is to be regarded as the true density of a cellulose fibre.

The argument put forward by Hermans in rejecting the density in helium as the true density of cellulose is based on the high density which would have to be attributed to the absorbed water. Thus he estimates, from the difference between the density in helium and in water, that the density of the absorbed water would be greater than 2.

Admittedly, this value is very high and would indicate the existence of enormous compressive forces. Stamm and Hansen (*5*), on the other hand, obtained a density for soda-boiled cotton-linter α-cellulose (a very pure form of cellulose) of 1·588 at 20°C, which approaches that of crystalline native cellulose (1·592). Based on this density in helium, the density of the absorbed water at the fibre saturation point (24% moisture regain) would be 1·035, which is an entirely reasonable value. We still have to explain the different densities found for cotton in helium by Davidson (1·567) and by Stamm (1·588). A clue is provided by some work done by Wakeham (*6*), who measured the density of different kinds of cotton in benzene, dioctyl phthalate and mercury. He found that, if the fibres were cut by grinding in a ball mill and passed through a 20-mesh screen, the density of the cut fibres was always greater than that of the whole fibres. On the average, an increase in density of 0·021 was obtained for cut cotton fibres measured in benzene and in dioctyl phthalate. Now, Davidson (*1*) used whole cotton fibres, whereas Stamm and Hansen (*5*) used cut fibres. Assuming that a closer approach to the true density of the cellulose substance will be given by cut fibres—more pores will be made accessible—Davidson's values for the density of cotton in helium can be corrected to give a density of 1·588 for native American cotton, which agrees with the value obtained by Stamm and Hansen, and which is very close to the density of crystalline native cellulose. Thus it seems reasonable to conclude that the density as calculated from X-ray data may be taken as the true density of dry cellulose ; the value for the dry cellulose fibre determined in helium approaches this true density very closely.

Hermans (*7*) prefers an alternative approach to the concept of the density of a fibre. He argues that the macroscopic concepts of density become meaningless when extrapolated to the order of magnitude of molecular dimensions. In other words, the volume of a porous body can be measured only by using molecules that are considerably smaller than the dimensions of the pores in the body. Since the density of fibres in benzene, toluene, carbon tetrachloride, and similar non-swelling liquids is the same, although the size of these molecules varies, this density may be regarded as the 'macroscopic' density of the fibre. This 'macroscopic' density is regarded by Hermans as the real density of the material and it has been used a great deal in his studies of moisture regain and optical properties of cellulose fibres.

Before leaving this brief discussion of the concept of density, it should be pointed out that if the medium used to determine density has appreciably larger molecules than those of benzene, toluene, carbon tetrachloride, etc., then a lower fibre density will be obtained. Thus, in Table 12 are recorded average values obtained in benzene and in dioctyl phthalate, for five samples of cotton. For both whole and cut fibres the density in dioctyl phthalate is significantly less than

TABLE 12

DENSITY OF FIVE COTTONS

Medium / Form of fibre	Density (g/cm^3)	
	Benzene	Dioctyl phthalate
Whole	1·540	1·516
Cut (20 mesh)	1·554	1·542

that in benzene: this may be interpreted to mean that the very large molecules of dioctyl phthalate do not penetrate into the pores of the fibres so completely as do the molecules of benzene.

DENSITY AND MOISTURE REGAIN

The relationships between the density, measured in a non-swelling medium such as toluene, and the moisture regain of various fibres are shown by the continuous lines in *Figure 68* (the dashed lines represent the densities of the fibres measured in water). A characteristic feature of all the curves obtained with a non-swelling medium is the initial increase in density which accompanies the absorption of small amounts of water, followed by a fall in density as more water is absorbed, i.e., the density–regain curve passes through a maximum, which occurs at 3–12% moisture regain, depending on the type of fibre. The same density–regain curve applies to both absorption and desorption conditions.

One might have expected the density of the moist fibre to fall steadily from a maximum value at zero regain, since the density of water is less than that of the dry fibre. This is not so, however, and it remains to explain the initial increase in density. Two possible explanations have been put forward: (*a*) that the absorbed water is compressed and (*b*) that the absorbed water enters pores in the structure which were not entered by the non-swelling medium (e.g., benzene or toluene) in which the fibre densities were measured. Probably both explanations are partially correct. One would certainly expect water molecules to penetrate the fibre pores more completely than would the molecules of benzene, for example, because of their smaller size, their chemical affinity for cellulose, and the swelling which may make available for occupation spaces which in the dry state of the fibre were too small to be entered.

A clearer picture of the process may be obtained by plotting the volume occupied by one gram of cellulose (the specific volume) against the moisture regain: this has been done in *Figure 69* (*see* Hermans (*7*)), the curves forming the top boundaries of the shaded

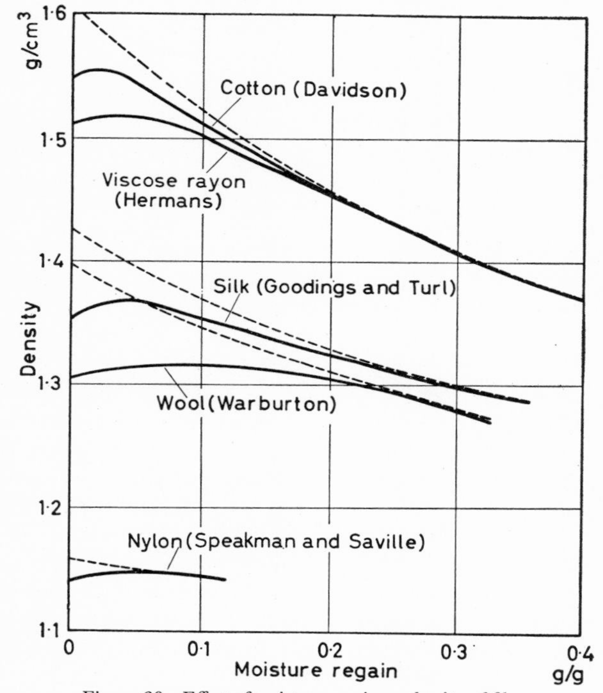

Figure 68. Effect of moisture regain on density of fibres

portions being the specific volume–regain relationships for fibres measured in a non-swelling medium such as benzene. As moisture is absorbed, the volume of the moist fibre is less than the volume of the dry fibre and added water taken separately, i.e., on absorbing water a contraction in total volume takes place. Before saturation regain has been reached, the rate of increase in volume of the moist fibre becomes equal to the volume of water absorbed. This occurs at about 10% regain for cotton and 20–25% regain for regenerated cellulose.

The initial specific volume of the dry fibre may be regarded formally as consisting of the volume occupied by the cellulose molecules and a certain fraction of empty space. If water molecules are absorbed and packed amongst the chain molecules, part of the empty space will be occupied by water and the increase in the volume of the fibre will generally be less than that calculated additively from the initial volumes of cellulose and water separately. Hence, macroscopically, a contraction will be observed. At a certain moisture

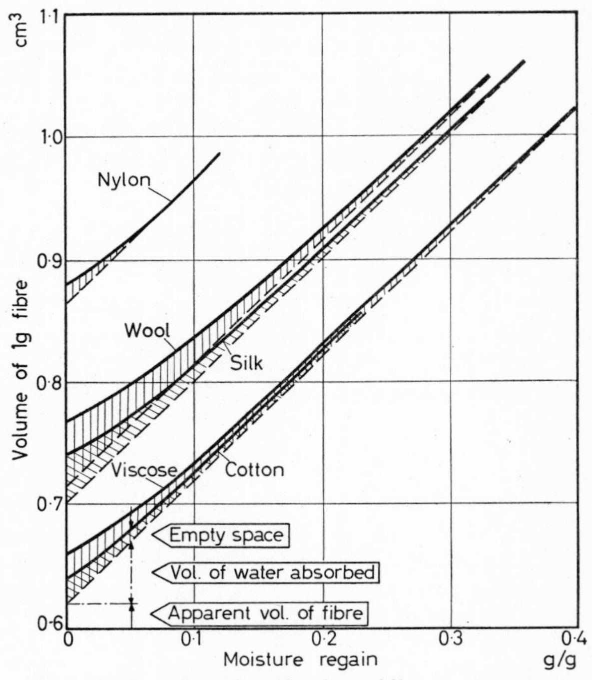

Figure 69. Dependence of specific volume of fibre on moisture regain (sources as for Fig. 68)

regain, when the chain molecules in the absorbing part of the fibre are covered with a monolayer of water molecules, no further occupation of initially empty space will occur, because any further water molecules entering the fibre will then be piled up against water molecules, just as they are in liquid water. Hence, no further contraction will occur. From this point onwards, the absorption assumes the character of capillary condensation.

The dashed line with a slope of 45° represents the sum of the volume of cellulose not accessible to water (labelled apparent volume of fibre in *Figure 69*)and the volume of water absorbed. The vertical distance between this line and the continuous line represents the volume of empty space still available and accessible to water. The intercept of the dashed line with the volume axis should be, and is found experimentally to be, equal to the reciprocal of the apparent density of the dry fibre measured in water.

When the optical properties of cellulose fibres are discussed, it will be seen that the proposition that the volume of moist cellulose fibres can be taken as being additively composed of three fractions, namely, cellulose, water and empty space, with densities equal to the apparent density of cellulose in water, unity and zero, respectively, will be used to explain the observed phenomena.

At this stage it will be instructive to examine the relation between moisture regain, swelling and density. The volume swelling (S_α) at fractional moisture regain α is given by

$$S_\alpha = \frac{(V_\alpha - V_0)}{V_0} . 100 = \left\{\frac{\rho_0(1+\alpha)}{\rho_\alpha} - 1\right\} 100 \qquad \ldots .(1)$$

where V_0 is the volume of dry fibre, V_α the volume of fibre with regain α, ρ_0 the density of dry fibre and ρ_α the density of fibre with regain α.

Consider, for example, the swelling of wool in water. Here $\rho_0 = 1 \cdot 304$, $\alpha = 0 \cdot 33$ at 100% r.h. and $\rho_\alpha = 1 \cdot 271$, so that $S_\alpha = 36 \cdot 3\%$, which is almost identical with the value of 36·8% found directly by Warburton (*8*).

From *Figure 69*, it will readily be appreciated that the apparent volume of the fibre in water is given by the apparent volume of the dry fibre plus the volume of absorbed water. It follows that the apparent specific volume in water (v'_α) of the moist fibre at regain α (g water/g fibre) is given by

$$(1+\alpha) . v'_\alpha = 1 . v'_0 + \alpha . 1 \qquad \ldots .(2)$$

if the density of absorbed water is taken as unity.

As an example of the application of equation (2), we can calculate the moisture regain from the apparent specific volume in water of the conditioned and the dry fibre. Consider a sample of cotton that has been conditioned to 65% r.h.; then $v'_{65} = 0 \cdot 647$, and after drying the fibre, $v'_0 = 0 \cdot 621$, whence from equation (2)

$$\alpha = \frac{v'_\alpha - v'_0}{1 - v'_\alpha} = 0 \cdot 069$$

or its moisture regain is 6·9%, which agrees with the figure of 7·0% read from the absorption isotherm at 65% r.h.

The relationship between the density of dry staple fibre rayons, cotton and ramie and their swelling in water has been investigated by Elöd and Fröhlich (*9*) and some of their results are given in *Figure 70*. Point 1 refers to ramie, point 2 to cotton. As the density of the dry fibres increases the amount of swelling decreases. The dry densities were measured in carbon tetrachloride by using a specific gravity bottle and the swelling in water was calculated as the weight

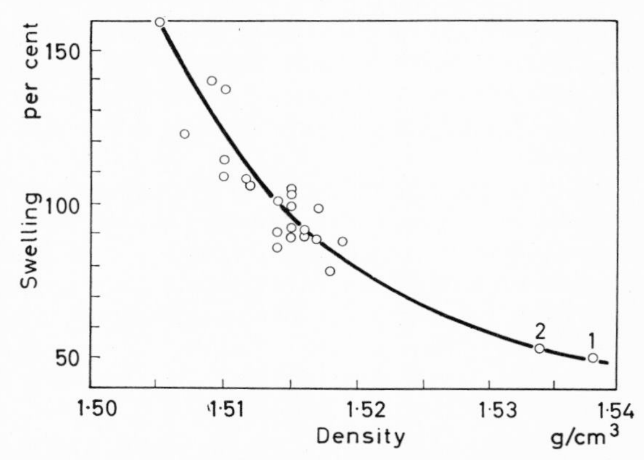

Figure 70. Relation of swelling of cellulosic fibres to density (after Elöd and Fröhlich (9))

of water retained, as a percentage of the dry weight, when the fibres had been centrifuged for 1 minute at an acceleration of 750,000 cm/sec².

INFLUENCE OF FIBRE STRUCTURE ON DENSITY

If it is assumed that the density of the amorphous regions in native and regenerated cellulose is the same, the ratio of the amorphous fraction in native cellulose to that in regenerated cellulose can be calculated from the specific volumes of native (v_n), regenerated (v_r) and crystalline cellulose (v_x). Let x_n and x_r be the amorphous fractions in native and regenerated cellulose, and v_m be the specific volume of amorphous cellulose. The volume of one gram of native cellulose is

$$v_n = x_n . v_m + (1 - x_n)\, v_x \qquad \ldots .(3)$$

and of regenerated cellulose

$$v_r = x_r . v_m + (1 - x_r)\, v_x \qquad \ldots .(4)$$

whence the ratio of amorphous fractions in regenerated and native cellulose is

$$x_r/x_n = (v_r - v_x)/(v_n - v_x) \quad \ldots.(5)$$

Taking the specific volumes to be the reciprocals of the densities of cut fibres measured in benzene, i.e., $v_r = 0{\cdot}658$, $v_n = 0{\cdot}641$ and $v_x = 0{\cdot}632$ and $0{\cdot}628$ for regenerated and native cellulose, respectively, it follows that $x_r/x_n = 2{\cdot}0$, which is about the same as the sorption ratio and supports the theory that the water-absorbing capacity of cellulose fibres depends on the amount of amorphous cellulose present. For mercerized ramie the specific volume is $0{\cdot}654$, so that $x_r/x_n = 1{\cdot}7$, whilst the sorption ratio is $1{\cdot}6$; again the agreement is excellent.

If the density of the amorphous part were known, it would be possible to make an approximate estimation from equations (3) and (4) of the percentage of amorphous material in each kind of fibre. Biltz (*10*) has found a difference of 6% between the specific volume of butyl alcohol in the crystalline and in the amorphous state and, assuming the same difference for cellulose, $v_m - v_x = 0{\cdot}038$. The amorphous fractions would then be 34%, 58% and 68% for cotton, mercerized ramie and viscose rayon, respectively. These values agree with estimates made by Hermans (*7*, p. 182) from optical and X-ray data.

One would expect that the larger the amount of crystalline material in a fibre, the higher would be the density of the dry substance. The density in water, however, depends on the density of packing in the system cellulose–water, which is presumably largest in the amorphous parts, so that for similar materials, those with higher dry densities would be expected to have lower densities in water. *Figure 71* shows that this conclusion is borne out by the experimental data on regenerated cellulose fibres.

The values of density in water found by Hermans (*7*, p. 96) are significantly higher than those found by other investigators. This is most likely due to the fact that Hermans always used fresh material that had not previously been dried at elevated temperatures; previous drying at high temperatures in air (100°C) is known to reduce the density in water by 3 to 5 units in the third decimal place, or by about $0{\cdot}25\%$. Similarly, the moisture regain of cotton fibres that have not previously been dried is higher than that of fibres that have been dried. Drying at 100°C increases the dry density and reduces the moisture regain at any given relative humidity.

Hermans also took precautions to eliminate all traces of air by evacuating the system in the presence of water vapour and then boiling the fibres in air-free water for 16 hours before cooling and making the measurements of density by means of a hydrostatic balance. He found that the final equilibrium swelling was reached only very slowly and that it was a function of the temperature of the water. This phenomenon appears to be bound up with the slow change in structure which was postulated by Crank in an earlier chapter to account for the results of his diffusion experiments.

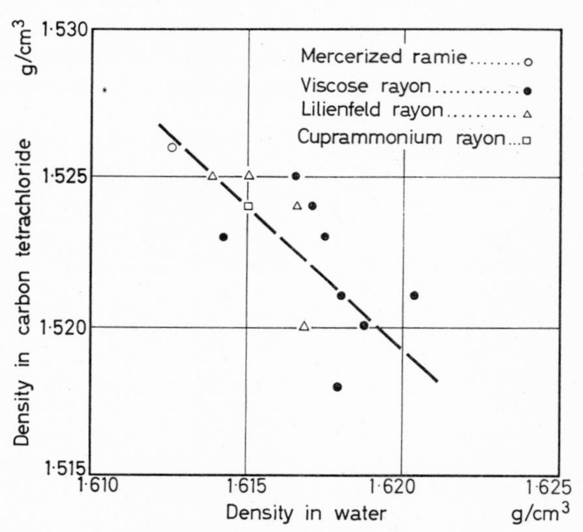

Figure 71. Dry and wet density of regenerated cellulose fibres (after Hermans (7))

It is well known that ordinary viscose rayons have a skin of varying thickness which stains a different colour from the core of the fibre when cross-sections are dyed with Victoria Blue. A technique suggested by Elöd & Fröhlich (*9*) can be applied to 'peel-off' outer layers of the filament. This consists in converting the outer layer of the filaments into cellulose triacetate by controlled topochemical acetylation, followed by removal of the acetylated layer by means of a solvent for the triacetate. In this way successive layers would be peeled-off up to 60% of the weight of the fibre. Hermans (*11*) has applied this method to viscose and cuprammonium rayons and has measured the density, molecular orientation, swelling and mechanical properties of the treated filaments. He shows that the acid catalyst used in the process may affect the physical properties of the treated fibres, but concludes that orientation is unaffected and density only slightly affected, if at all, so that the observed radial gradient in orientation and density is real, whereas the evidence on true differences in swelling power remains uncertain.

Figure 72 shows the density of dry filaments of viscose rayon plotted against the amount of material peeled off. It will be seen that the density increases towards the core of the fibre (contrary to the results of Elöd & Fröhlich (*9*)). The solid symbols are the result of direct determinations of density by a flotation method in carbon tetrachloride, whilst the open symbols represent densities calculated from the optical properties of the fibres. The fact that the two different methods of obtaining the density lead to the same result lends

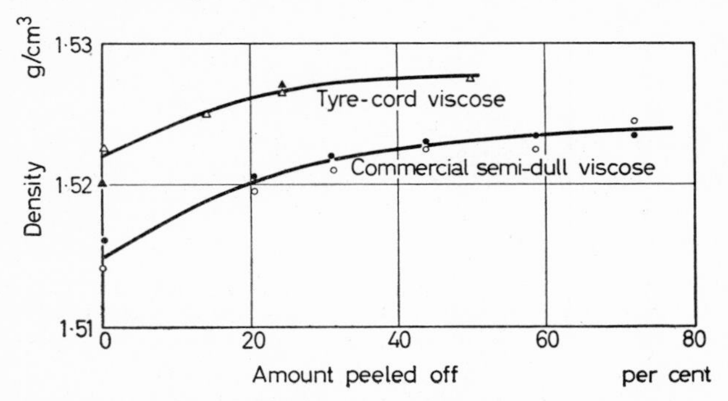

Figure 72. Relation between density of viscose rayon filaments and amount peeled off (after Hermans (11))

support to the validity of the observed variation in density from the outside to the inside of the fibre. It will be shown presently how density is related to optical properties. For cuprammonium rayon, the variation in density from the outside to the inside of the fibre was found to be almost negligible ($1 \cdot 525_5$ for the untreated fibre and $1 \cdot 527_5$ with 48% peeled off. The density of the removed skin (ρ_s) can be calculated from the fraction (x) peeled off, the density of the original fibre (ρ) and the density of the core (ρ_c) reduced by 4×10^{-3} to allow for the average modification due to acid treatment. Thus, adding volumes,

$$1/\rho - (1-x)/\rho_c = x/\rho_s \qquad \ldots . (6)$$

It is found from this equation that the increase in density, when about half the fibre has been peeled off, varies from 0 to 1% depending on the type of rayon.

DYEING AND THE DENSITY OF FIBRES

Some measurements have been made by Heertjes (*12*) on the effect of dyeing with direct dyes on the density of cotton, silk and wool. It would be expected that the amount of 'empty space' would influence the amount of dye bound within the fibre.

TABLE 13

SPECIFIC VOLUME (cm^3/g) OF FIBRES IN BENZENE AND IN WATER AT 20°C

Fibre	Specific volume		Empty space cm^3/g dry fibre
	in benzene	in water	
Cotton	0·655	0·625	0·030
,, dyed	0·655	0·625	0·030
Silk	0·750	0·710	0·040
,, dyed	0·757	0·718	0·039
Wool	0·768	0·723	0·045
,, dyed	0·773	0·725	0·048

In Table 13, the specific volumes of cotton, silk, and wool fibres before and after dyeing, as measured by Heertjes (*12*), are recorded. The specific volumes of the dyed fibres have been corrected for the amount of dye absorbed. The difference between the specific volume of the dry fibres in benzene and in water gives the volume of empty space per gram of dry fibre. It will be seen from the last column in the table that this is unchanged by dyeing cotton or silk but is increased by dyeing wool. Heertjes interprets this to mean that the dyeing process has not altered the water-binding power of the cotton and silk but has increased the water-binding power of wool. This follows if water which occupies the empty volume in the originally dry fibre is considered as 'bound', i.e., chemically held, water.

Another interesting relation between density and dyeing has been demonstrated by Feubel and Hilgers (*13*), who studied the differences in density which occur along the length of regenerated cellulose fibres. They result from differential drying of the fibre and lead to differences in dyeing properties. The density changes can be strikingly demonstrated by staining the fibre with a yellow Naphthol dye and examining it under the microscope: dark spots (where the looser parts of the fibre stain more deeply) can easily be seen. These do not disappear when the yarn is stretched and correspond to places where maximum swelling occurs in the fibre in cuprammonium solution. The optimum conditions for producing a fibre of uniform (high) density with correspondingly high resistance to swelling have been determined. This is done by drying the fibre at 260–270°C in the absence of air for a very short time.

DOUBLE REFRACTION, REFRACTIVE POWER AND DENSITY

Turning now to the relation between the optical properties and the moisture regain of fibres, it is necessary first to define double refraction and refractive power. Ordinary cellulose fibres are anisotropic and behave optically like a uniaxial crystal. The optic axis is parallel to the fibre axis and the refractive index depends on the direction of the plane of polarization of the incident light with respect to the fibre axis. When the light is plane polarized with the electric vector vibrating parallel to the fibre axis, the refractive index ($n_{\parallel}$) is a maximum, whereas when the electric vector is vibrating perpendicular to the fibre axis, the refractive index ($n_{\perp}$) is a minimum. The difference between these two refractive indices, ($n_{\parallel} - n_{\perp}$), is equal to the double refraction. It is given by

$$n_{\parallel} - n_{\perp} = \gamma\lambda/l \qquad \ldots.(7)$$

where γ is the phase difference between light waves polarized parallel and perpendicular to the fibre axis when they emerge from the fibre, λ is the wavelength of the light used and l is the thickness of the fibre. The double refraction can be determined either by measuring the two refractive indices separately or by measuring the phase difference with a compensator and the fibre thickness. Since most fibres are irregular in cross-section the measurement of refractive indices is usually preferred.

The state of orientation of the chain molecules in a fibre governs the double refraction and if it is desired to compare the *refractive power* of various fibres, the effect of orientation has to be eliminated without any change in density of packing. As a measure of refractive power (n_{iso}) we can take

$$n_{iso} = \tfrac{1}{3}(n_{\parallel} + 2n_{\perp}) \qquad \ldots.(8)$$

This equation expresses the refractive power of any fibre as a single constant, independent of orientation. According to a well-established empirical law due to Gladstone and Dale, *the quantity* $(n-1)/\rho$ *should be constant* for a given substance. In order to apply this law to fibres, the density and refractive power should be measured under corresponding conditions, i.e., in both cases with the aid of immersion media which do not penetrate into the fibre substance. It has been found by Hermans (*7*, p. 113) that $(n_{iso}-1)/\rho$ is constant for native and regenerated cellulose fibres; it is equal to 0·357 with a probable error of 0·0006. Applying Gladstone and Dale's law to $n_{\parallel}$ and $n_{\perp}$ separately we have

$$(n_{\parallel}-1)/\rho = \text{constant}, \quad (n_{\perp}-1)/\rho = \text{constant}$$

Hence,
$$(n_{\parallel}-n_{\perp})/\rho = \text{constant} \qquad \ldots.(9)$$

Thus, the refractive indices and the double refraction of various fibres with different densities can be compared. If the double refraction at one density is known, the double refraction at another density can be calculated: the converse of this was used to obtain the calculated densities in *Figure 72* (p. 151) from the observed double refraction.

INFLUENCE OF MOISTURE REGAIN ON OPTICAL PROPERTIES

Some of the earliest measurements of the variation of refractive index with moisture regain were made by Meyer and Frey-Wyssling

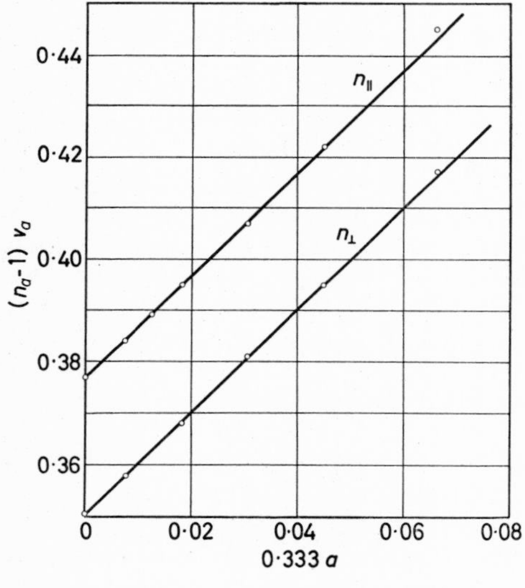

Figure 73. Relation between refractive index and volume of cellulose and volume of water absorbed (after Hermans et al. (15))

(*14*) on ramie fibres. They found that both $n_{\parallel}$ and $n_{\perp}$ decreased very slightly as the moisture regain increased; the results were not in agreement with any one of a number of formulæ that might be expected to give the refractive index of a mixture of two components with different refractive indices.

Starting from the observation that the refractive index of dry fibres conforms to Gladstone and Dale's formula $(n_{iso}-1)/\rho = \text{constant}$, it follows that, for a given mass of substance with refractive index n and volume v, the same amount of substance with volume v' will have a refractive index n' given by the equation

$$(n'-1)\,v' = (n-1)\,v \qquad \ldots.(10)$$

Hermans, Hermans and Vermaas (*15*) have applied Gladstone and Dale's law to moist cellulose as follows. Let 1 g of dry cellulose with volume v_0 absorb a g of water and acquire a volume v_a: then the contribution of the cellulose to the refractivity of the gel will be $(n_0-1)\,v_0/v_a$. Since the refractive index of water at 20°C is 1·333 and its volume is a, the contribution of the water to the refractivity of the gel is $0{\cdot}3333a/v_a$. The total refractivity is therefore

$$n_a-1 = (n_0-1)\,.\,v_0/v_a+0{\cdot}3333a/v_a$$

or

$$(n_a-1)\,v_a = (n_0-1)\,v_0+0{\cdot}3333a \qquad \ldots.(11)$$

Plotting $(n_a-1)\,v_a$ against $0{\cdot}333a$ for stretched model filaments of regenerated cellulose, as in *Figure 73*, shows that the observed points lie on straight lines with unit slope, indicating that equation (11) applies to both $n_\parallel$ and $n_\perp$ for these filaments; i.e.,

$$(n_\parallel-1)_a\cdot v_a = (n_\perp-1)_0\cdot v_0+0{\cdot}3333a$$

$$(n_\parallel-1)_a\cdot v_a = (n_\perp-1)_0\cdot v_0+0{\cdot}3333a$$

from which it can be seen that

$$(n_\parallel-n_\perp)_a = (n_\parallel-n_\perp)_0\cdot v_0/v_a \qquad \ldots.(12)$$

Since $v_a/v_0 = q$, the degree of swelling, we may write

$$(n_\parallel-n_\perp)_a = (n_\parallel-n_\perp)_0/q \qquad \ldots.(13)$$

i.e., *the double refraction of the fibre is inversely proportional to its degree of swelling.*

This relationship assumes that the double refraction of the moist fibre is determined by that of the cellulose alone. The water is absorbed in the amorphous parts of the fibre where it is uniformly distributed and the moist fibre has the properties of a solution of water in cellulose.

Figure 74 shows the refractive index of anisotropic model filaments of cellulose plotted against moisture regain a (g water per g dry fibre). The circles represent the experimental points and the continuous line is the curve calculated according to equation (11), i.e., assuming Gladstone and Dale's law for mixtures.

It has been known for some time that the optical behaviour of cellulose fibres immersed in various liquids is in qualitative agreement with the theory of anisotropic mixed bodies developed by Wiener (*16*). According to this theory the double refraction of an orientated cellulose fibre must be ascribed to two superimposed components, one due to the *optical anisotropy of the cellulose itself* and the other due to the particular arrangement of the cellulose crystallites in the fibre, known as *structural birefringence*. This second component depends exclusively on the refractive power of the cellulose and that of the

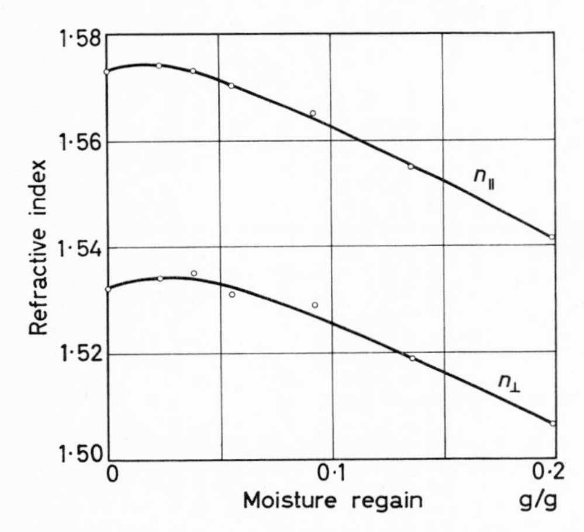

Figure 74. Dependence of refractive index of anisotropic cellulose monofils on moisture regain (after Hermans et al. (*15*))

swelling medium and on the volume fractions of the two. According to Wiener this component is given by the equations

$$n_{\parallel}^2 = V_1 n_1^2 + (1 - V_1)\, n_2^2 \qquad \ldots.(14)$$

$$n_{\perp}^2 = n_2^2 \left[\frac{(1 + V_1)\, n_1^2 + (1 - V_1)\, n_2^2}{(1 + V_1)\, n_2^2 + (1 - V_1)\, n_1^2}\right] \qquad \ldots.(15)$$

where n_1 and n_2 are the refractive indices of the cellulose and of the swelling medium, respectively, and V_1 is the fractional volume of cellulose in unit volume of swollen fibre.

The results of measuring the double refraction of ramie fibres in various liquids are shown in *Figure 75*, due to Frey-Wyssling and Speich (*17*). The curve obtained with aldehydes and alcohols is typical of the effect to be expected from equations (14) and (15). The minimum occurs at a refractive index of liquid equal to that of the cellulose, and the double refraction at this point is equal to the *intrinsic birefringence* of the cellulose. For liquids with higher or lower refractive index, the *structural birefringence* is added to the intrinsic birefringence. It should be noted that, in non-polar liquids, the double refraction is constant. This is interpreted to mean that such liquids are not absorbed by the cellulose and therefore produce no swelling and no structural birefringence; *hence the use of such liquids for determining the real macroscopic density of fibres.*

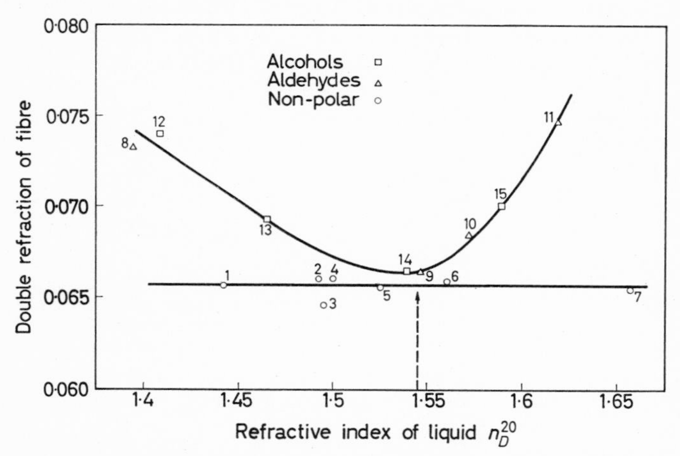

Figure 75. Double refraction of ramie fibres in various liquids (after Frey-Wyssling and Speich (17))

For the swelling of cellulose fibres in water we can introduce the degree of swelling (q), instead of the fractional volume (V_1). Thus,

$$V_1 = 1/q, \quad 1-V_1 = (q-1)/q \qquad \ldots.(16)$$

and, substituting for V_1 and $1-V_1$ in equations (14) and (15), the double refraction arising from the structural birefringence can be calculated for any degree of swelling. The value of n_1 which should be substituted in this case is the average value of $(n_{\parallel})_0$ and $(n_{\perp})_0$ and $n_2 = 1 \cdot 3333$, the refractive index of water. Denoting the structural component of double refraction thus found by $(n_{\parallel}-n_{\perp})_w$, the total double refraction of the swollen fibre becomes

$$(n_{\parallel}-n_{\perp})_q = \frac{(n_{\parallel}-n_{\perp})_0}{q} + (n_{\parallel}-n_{\perp})_w \qquad \ldots.(17)$$

Since it has already been shown that up to 15% moisture regain for orientated regenerated cellulose monofilaments, equation (13) holds good (*Figure 74*), it is concluded that for low regains the structural birefringence is zero. It may be responsible, however, for the small discrepancy of about 2×10^{-3} units which was observed at 20% regain (*Figure 74*, p. 156) and 4×10^{-3} units at 78% regain. The calculated Wiener components of birefringence for these two regains are 6×10^{-3} and 9×10^{-3} units, respectively, which are too large. The explanation of this would appear to be that it is assumed in Wiener's theory that the components of cellulose and water are separated by a well-defined interface, layers of cellulose several molecules thick alternating with thick layers of water molecules. This is not unreasonable at high moisture regains. However, if the crystallites of cellulose are regarded as being embedded in a homogeneous medium consisting of amorphous cellulose and water, the change in refractive index in passing from the crystallites to the surrounding phase will not be so great as it would if the surrounding phase were pure water, and the smaller Wiener birefringence would be accounted for.

So far, we have considered the relation between refractive index and regain for regenerated cellulose monofils, and its theoretical interpretation. The theory also applies to ramie fibres and commercial rayons, as shown by the data (from Hermans (7) in Table 14, where the refractive index ($n_{\parallel}$ or $n_{\perp}$) as observed at 65% r.h. and at zero regain is recorded, together with the refractive indices of the bone-dry fibres calculated from those at 65% r.h. The agreement of observed and calculated values is reasonably good.

TABLE 14

REFRACTIVE INDICES OF DRY FIBRES, CALCULATED AND OBSERVED

Specimen	Refractive index					
	at 65% r.h.		bone dry			
	observed		calculated		observed	
	$n_{\parallel}$	$n_{\perp}$	$n_{\parallel}$	$n_{\perp}$	$n_{\parallel}$	$n_{\perp}$
Ramie	1·595	1·526$_5$	1·601	1·532	1·602	1·532
Viscose, ordinary, low stretch	1·537$_5$	1·517	1·557$_5$	1·533$_5$	1·560	1·533$_5$
,, ,, high stretch	1·552	1·514	1·574$_5$	1·530$_5$	1·573	1·529
,, Lilienfeld	1·553	1·515	1·576	1·531	1·576	1·531
Bemberg rayon	1·549	1·518	1·571	1·535	1·572	1·535

It may be concluded that, as far as cellulose fibres are concerned, by considering the macroscopic density determined in non-swelling fluids as the real density, the effect of moisture on the density and optical properties can be accounted for in a simple way.

REFERENCES

1 G. F. Davidson, *J. Text. Inst.*, **18,** T175 (1927).
2 A. J. Stamm, *Text. Res. J.*, **20,** 631 (1950).
3 K. Lauer and U. Westerman, *Kolloid-Z*, **107,** 89 (1944).
4 P. H. Hermans, J. J. Hermans, D. Vermaas and A. Weidinger, *Rec. trav. chim.*, **63,** 44 (1944).
5 A. J. Stamm and L. A. Hansen, *J. Phys. Chem.*, **41,** 1007 (1937).
6 H. Wakeham, *Text. Res. J.*, **19,** 595 (1949).
7 P. H. Hermans, *Contribution to the Physics of Cellulose Fibres*, Elsevier, Amsterdam, 1946.
8 F. L. Warburton, *J. Text. Inst.*, **38,** T65 (1947).
9 E. Elöd and H. G. Fröhlich, *Melliand Textilber.*, **27,** 103 (1946); *Text. Res. J.*, **18,** 487 (1948).
10 W. Biltz, *Z. physik. Chem.*, **A151,** 13 (1930).
11 P. H. Hermans, *Text. Res. J.*, **20,** 553 (1950).
12 P. M. Heertjes, *Rec. trav. Chim.*, **61,** 751 (1942).
13 A. Feubel and F. Hilgers, *Melliand Textilber.*, **29,** 233 (1948).
14 M. Meyer and A. Frey-Wyssling, *Helv. Chim. Acta*, **18,** 1428 (1935).
15 P. H. Hermans, J. J. Hermans and D. Vermaas, *J. Colloid Sci.*, **1,** 251 (1946).
16 O. Wiener, *Abh. Sächs. Akad. d. Wiss. Math. phys. Kl.*, **32,** 507, 604 (1912).
17 A. Frey-Wyssling and H. Speich, *Helv. Chim. Acta*, **25,** 1474 (1942).

Chapter 12

EFFECT OF MOISTURE ON MECHANICAL PROPERTIES

By R. Meredith

In spite of the fact that moisture has a considerable influence on many mechanical properties that are of importance in the processing and use of textiles, information on the effect of moisture on certain properties is still lacking. However, this does not prevent us from discussing the available data and examining the theoretical interpretation of the observed effects where this has been attempted.

The properties to be discussed may be divided into two broad classes: (i) tensile properties, which arise when fibres or yarns are stretched, and (ii) torsional properties, arising from the twisting of fibres and depending essentially on the rigidity modulus or resistance to shear. Under tensile properties, the effect of moisture on such properties as Young's modulus, yield point, elastic recovery, strength, creep and relaxation will be considered. Under torsional properties, the influence of humidity on torque-twist curves, rigidity modulus, shear strength and relaxation of torque in twisted fibres will be discussed.

The units used for expressing stresses and moduli are either dyn/cm^2 or kilometres weight (km wt.). It may be noted that 10^8 dyn/cm$^2 = 0 \cdot 981\ \rho$ km wt., where ρ is the density of the fibre in g/cm^3. Kilometres weight and grams weight/tex are identical.

TENSILE PROPERTIES

Stress–strain relations

Since the tensile behaviour of textile fibres depends on such factors as temperature and time, as well as on the relative humidity of the surrounding atmosphere, it is necessary to keep the temperature constant whilst studying, for example, the effect of humidity on the stress–strain curves of various fibres, shown in *Figure 76*. These curves were obtained at a temperature of 20°C and a rate of extension such that rupture occurred in 10 to 30 seconds.

At the relative humidity increases all the fibres become more extensible, i.e., the stress–strain modulus (ratio of stress to strain) becomes smaller and the extension at break becomes larger. This is due to the absorbed water reducing the cohesion of the chain molecules in the amorphous regions of the fibre, the crystalline regions having been shown by X-rays to be unaffected in most cases when the fibre absorbs water. Only one-twentieth of the force required to stretch the bone-dry material by 2% is needed to stretch wet viscose rayon or wet casein fibre by the same amount. For silk, nylon and wool, the force required is about one-third of that needed to extend the wet fibre.

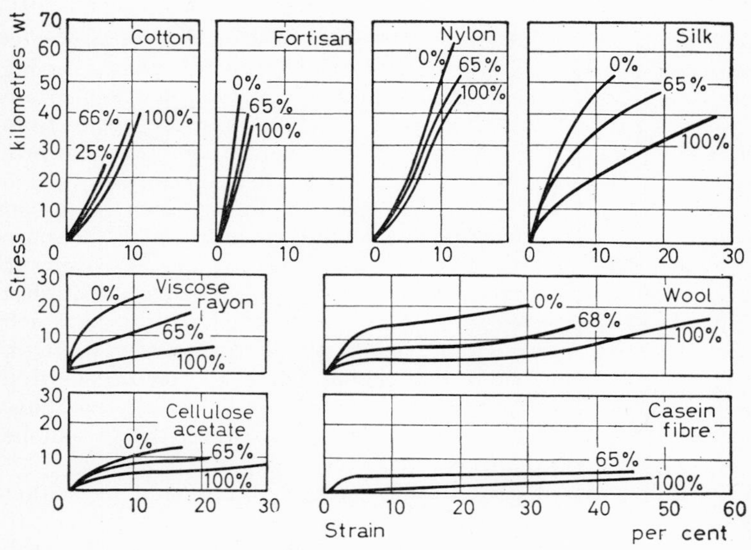

Figure 76. Effect of moisture on stress–strain curves of various fibres

When tested at 65% r.h., the more extensible fibres, such as viscose rayon, cellulose acetate, silk, wool, and casein fibre have stress–strain curves which show an initial linear part, with stress proportional to strain, followed by a gradual yielding of the fibre structure until the extension increases considerably for only a small increase in applied load. This effect is most pronounced in fibres such as wool and casein. An increase in the relative humidity produces a very large decrease in the stress at which the increased rate of extension sets in, and for some fibres (e.g., viscose rayon and casein), the 'yield' region has disappeared at 100% r.h., the fibre being easily extended by the smallest applied stress. In connection with this it is interesting to note the peculiar behaviour, recently observed by Farrow (*1*), of cellulose acetate when stretched after immersion in water at room temperature (*Figure 77*). Although an appreciable yield stress is observed when the fibre has been soaked in water for 24 hours before stretching, i.e., under equilibrium conditions, the yield stress is much smaller if the fibre is extended immediately after immersion in water. As the time of immersion is increased, the yield stress increases approximately in proportion to the logarithm of the time of immersion, and this additional stress disappears as the strain increases, so that a single stress–strain curve is followed for extensions greater than 20%. If the fibre were not fully swollen after only a few seconds immersion, the yield stress might be expected to fall with continued immersion, but the opposite effect is observed; also, studies of the diffusion of water

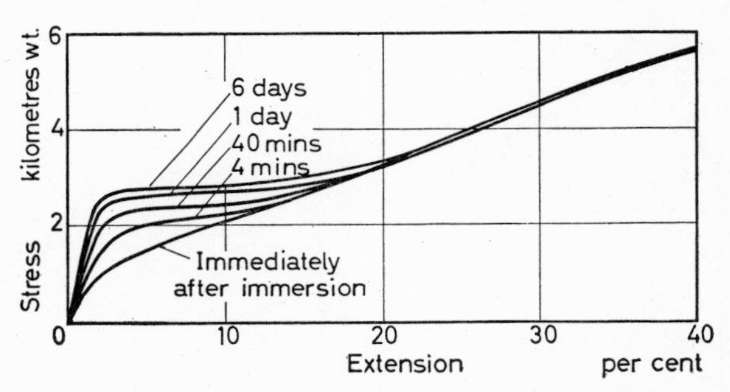

Figure 77. Increase in yield stress with immersion time for cellulose acetate yarn in water at 20°C (*after Farrow* (*1*))

into the fibre indicate that full penetration is obtained after only a few seconds. This peculiar behaviour indicates that secondary bonds, broken by swelling, gradually re-form over a comparatively long period (6 days).

To a first approximation, the stress–strain curve of ordinary viscose rayon in the wet state is a straight line, and Rose and Griffiths (*2*) have shown that the slope of this line is related to the structure of the fibre in a definite way. Thus, a series of almost 100 experimental rayons, produced by variations of the normal viscose process to give fibres having varying degrees of orientation, obeys the following equation:

$$i = \exp(a.\Delta n - b) \quad \ldots.(1)$$

where i is the average slope of the wet load–extension curve, Δn is the double refraction at 65% r.h. and a and b are constants. This equation holds for $\Delta n = 0\text{–}0{\cdot}035$, the corresponding slopes of the wet load–extension curves increasing by a factor of 170 in this range of double refraction.

Elastic recovery should be high if a textile fibre is to have stable dimensions and to remain serviceable. This property may be measured either as the ratio of the extension recovered to the extension imposed or by the ratio of the energy returned by the fibre to

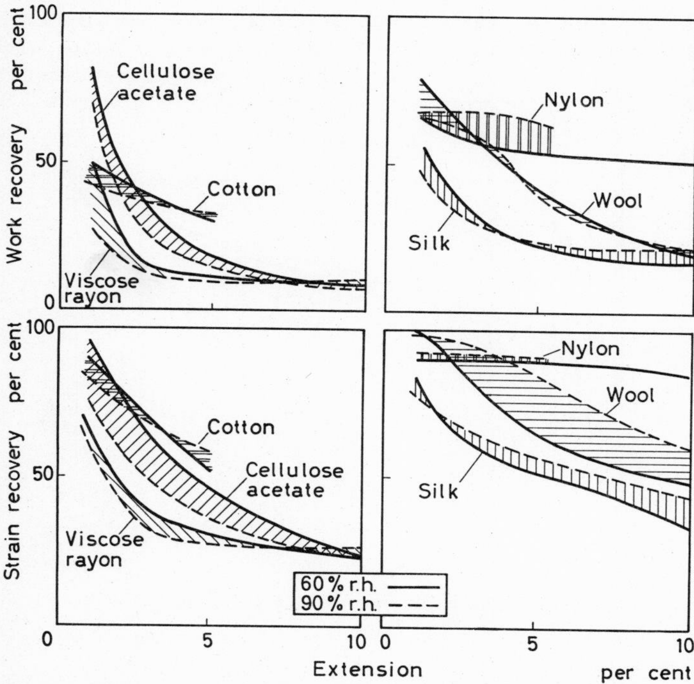

Figure 78. Elastic recovery of fibres at 60% and 90% r.h. (after Gagliardi and Gruntfast (19))

the energy absorbed by the fibre on stretching. In *Figure 78* both measures of elastic recovery have been plotted against extension for a number of different fibres at 60% and 90% r.h. For cellulose fibres, such as cotton, viscose rayon and cellulose acetate at 65% r.h., the elastic recovery decreases more rapidly as the extension is increased than it does with fibres such as wool, silk and nylon. The effect of increasing the relative humidity is to accentuate the difference between these two classes of fibre; in other words, increased relative humidity causes the elastic recovery of cellulose fibres to decrease, but the elastic recovery of wool, silk and nylon is increased by increasing the relative humidity.

Rupture

There is a striking difference between the effect of relative humidity on the tensile strength of native and regenerated cellulose fibres. This is illustrated by the curves shown in *Figure 79*, in which the strengths of different yarns measured at 65% r.h. are taken as the reference values and changes in strength with humidity are expressed

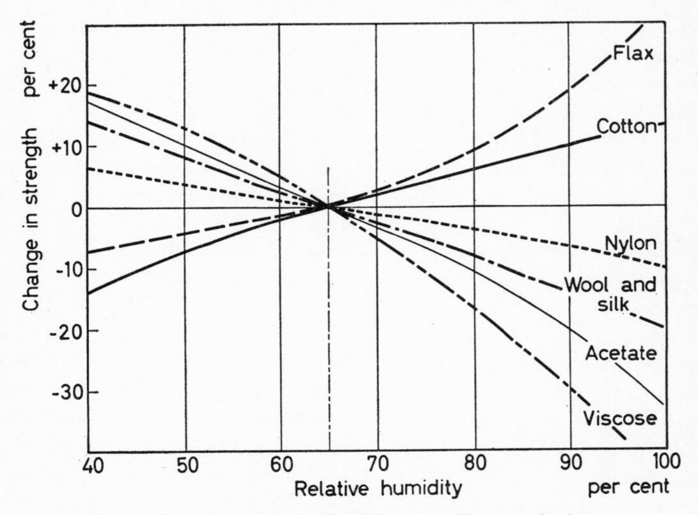

Figure 79. Effect of relative humidity on tensile strength of yarns

as a percentage of these values. In general, yarns made from native cellulose fibres are the only ones which show an increase in strength with increase in moisture regain; yarns made from all other kinds of fibre show either no effect (e.g., Terylene, Orlon) or a decrease in strength. In passing from 65% r.h. to the wet state, nylon loses about 10%, wool and silk about 20%, cellulose acetate about 30% and ordinary viscose rayon as much as 50% of the air-dry strength.

How is the contrary behaviour of native and regenerated cellulose fibres explained? Fundamentally, it is due to a different balance between the decrease in cohesive force between the chain molecules due to swelling and the release of internal strain by swelling. Thus, in the native cellulose fibres, such as cotton and flax, the release of internal strain between the long-chain molecules predominates and this increases the fibre strength because of a more uniform internal distribution of stress; in regenerated fibres, however, the absorbed water reduces the number of points of adhesion of the cellulose chain molecules and concentrates the stress on to a relatively small number of molecules, which fail by rupture. In support of this broad statement it should be noted that the average chain length (or degree of polymerization) in natural cellulose fibres is at least five times greater than that in regenerated cellulose, so that individual molecules in native cellulose fibres may be expected to have more points of adhesion and so to possess greater internal strain.

It is interesting to note that the strength of highly tendered cotton decreases with increase in relative humidity in a similar way to that of viscose rayon; this is probably due to rupture of some of the chain molecules in the non-crystalline regions during tendering, which leaves little internal strain to be released by the swelling action of the absorbed water. For the same degree of polymerization, the loss in strength is the same for native and regenerated cellulose fibres (*3*).

Although the data in *Figure 79* refer to yarns, the effects observed represent essentially the corresponding fibre behaviour. From humidity–strength data on single cotton fibres, there is a small difference in the behaviour of fibre and yarn above 65% r.h., for, whereas the cotton yarn continues to show a small increase in strength with increase in humidity, cotton fibres generally show no change. The different behaviour of fibre and yarn may be accounted for by the higher coefficient of friction between the fibres at the higher relative humidities and by the swelling of the fibres, which allows them to interlock more effectively. Since continuous-filament yarns made from nylon, silk, viscose rayon and cellulose acetate do not depend for their strength on inter-fibre friction, the effect of humidity on the strength of both fibre and yarn would be expected to be almost identical.

The strength of cellulose acetate is less sensitive to relative humidity changes than that of ordinary viscose rayon, because of the smaller number of available hydroxyl groups and the lower degree of swelling. Highly orientated viscose rayon is also less sensitive to relative humidity than is ordinary viscose rayon. For example, the relative loss in strength is 40–55% for viscose rayon of a moderate degree of orientation, but for highly orientated viscose rayons the loss is 12–35%.

The dependence on relative humidity of the breaking extension of yarns made from a number of fibres is shown in *Figure 80*. Again the breaking extension at 65% r.h. is taken as a reference value and changes in breaking extension are expressed as a percentage of this value. In each case the breaking extension increases with increase in relative humidity, the increase from 65% to 100% r.h. being 18% for cellulose acetate, 25% for silk, and intermediate in value for viscose rayon, flax and cotton. Wool is outstanding in that the breaking extension increases by as much as 50%.

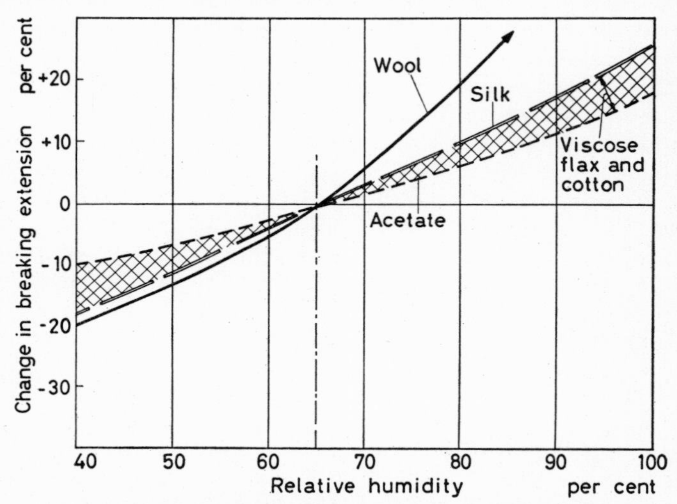

Figure 80. Effect of relative humidity on breaking extension of yarns

Creep

So far we have been concerned with the effect of moisture on tensile properties measured with either constant rate of loading or constant rate of extension, i.e., the effect of time has been controlled but not investigated. There are two other broad types of experiment which can be made to study the influence of time; one consists in holding the material under a constant load or stress and measuring the resulting increase in extension with time, which is called *creep*, and the other consists in extending the material quickly by a given amount and following the decrease in tension with time at constant length, called *relaxation*. Although there is a fair amount of information available on the creep and relaxation of fibres, very little systematic work has been done on the effect of humidity on these properties.

Some early work by Steinberger (*4*) on the effect of relative humidity on the creep of cellulose acetate filaments and cuprammonium rayon filaments was done with a constant load equivalent to about half the normal breaking stress. The effect on the creep of cellulose acetate of increasing the relative humidity in steps of about 10% can be seen from *Figure 81*; similar results were obtained with cuprammonium rayon. The dry fibres show an immediate elastic extension followed by a slow creep, which in magnitude exceeds the elastic extension only after a considerable time. There is not much change in behaviour up to 40% r.h., but when the experiment is made at 60–70%, i.e., in the region of the standard atmosphere for

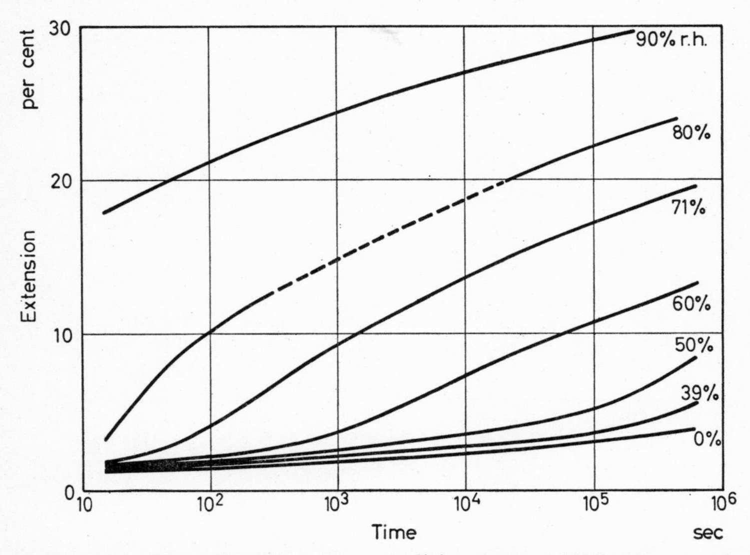

Figure 81. Effect of humidity on creep of cellulose acetate at 20°C under stress of $6 \cdot 5 \times 10^8$ dyn/cm² (based on data by Steinberger (4))

testing textiles (65% r.h.), creep forms the major part of the total extension after only a short time. At 90% r.h., the highest humidity for which results are given, much creep had already taken place within the first 15 seconds before observations were started. In the time range of the observations, the creep curves above 70% r.h. show no sign of reaching a limiting extension before the filament ruptures. The appearance of the whole family of curves suggests that each one may be part of a common sigmoidal curve which is shifted parallel to the time axis towards shorter times as the relative humidity is increased.

Leaderman (*5*) has obtained similar creep curves for nylon under a small constant load ($1 \cdot 8 \times 10^8$ dyn/cm²), as shown in *Figure 82*.

The constant 'load' used was smaller than that used with cellulose acetate filaments and the resulting extensions were much smaller, but the general appearance of the shape of the creep (and creep recovery) curves is the same. The dry filaments show very little creep, whilst those conditioned at 62% r.h. have a sigmoidal creep curve with creep forming the greater part of the total extension within the time range 50–50,000 seconds, and those conditioned at 100% r.h.

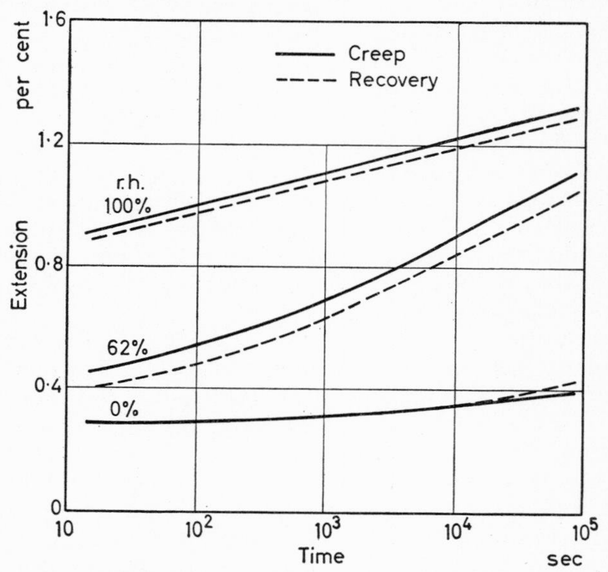

Figure 82. Creep and creep recovery of nylon at 20°C under stress of $1 \cdot 8 \times 10^8$ dyn/cm² (after Leaderman (5))

show less creep than ones conditioned at 62% r.h., at least within the observed range of time.

Holland, Halsey and Eyring (*6*) have attempted to analyse some creep curves obtained for filaments of viscose rayon at 9 to 100% r.h. Briefly, they found that the curves for primary creep (recoverable) could be fitted by an application of Eyring's theory of rate processes. This theory is based on the idea that the segments of the chain molecules in a polymer are continually moving relative to each other due to thermal energy; the application of a stress reduces the amount of thermal energy necessary for a segment of a molecule to surmount the potential barrier separating its equilibrium positions and so causes a measurable external strain to occur in the direction of the applied stress. The energy that must be given to a segment of a molecule in order that it can pass over the potential barrier into the next equilibrium position is called the energy of activation. Activation energies for the flow process calculated by means of this theory were found to decrease as the relative humidity increased. This result is sensible enough although the values of activation energy at the different relative humidities show considerable scatter and it is not always clear where the primary creep (recoverable) ends and secondary creep (permanent) begins.

The data obtained by Steinberger for cellulose acetate (*Figure 81*, p. 167) have been analysed by Reichardt, Halsey and Eyring (*7*). They found that, as the relative humidity increased, the energy of activation decreased, from about 33 kcal/mole at 39% r.h. to 21 kcal/mole at 80% r.h. The precise meaning to be attached to these figures is not clear, because, apart from the uncertainty in fixing the values of extension at which primary creep ceases, it would not be expected that the behaviour of the fibre could be represented at the higher strains by the theory used, which assumes complete reversibility; this is not observed.

By wetting and reconditioning fibres to remove internal strains, it is possible to shed further light on the question of how much of the strain produced by creep under constant load is elastic, i.e., completely recoverable, and how much represents a permanent change in the fibre. From this point of view, Press (*8*) has studied the flow and recovery properties of a viscose rayon yarn at 65% r.h. and 70°F under a wide range of 'loads' for times of up to a million seconds. The recovery of the viscose rayon varied with the range of total extension, and up to at least 12% could be roughly divided into three ranges: 0–$\frac{3}{4}$%, $\frac{3}{4}$–4%, and above 4%. Extensions up to $\frac{3}{4}$% total extension are retarded but completely elastic. This range represents the maximum movement of molecular segments before weaker secondary bonds in the relatively amorphous regions begin to break. In the second range, from $\frac{3}{4}$% to 4%, extension is not completely recoverable until the sample is swollen in water. Molecular-chain segments have begun to change position but do not have sufficient translational and rotational energy to move into new equilibrium positions of *strong* interaction. Swelling in water reduces the steric hindrance and allows the weakened restoring forces to bring the segments back to their original state of lower order. Above 4%, the extensions are not completely recoverable even after swelling in water. The further decrease in viscosity with breakage of additional secondary bonds in the amorphous regions is overshadowed by the increase in internal viscosity resulting from some molecular segments now having sufficient translational and rotational energy to move into stable equilibrium positions.

Relaxation

When a fibre is stretched and held at constant length, the tension relaxes by the same mechanism that causes the fibre to creep under constant load. Speakman (*9*) has investigated the effect of relative humidity on the relaxation of wool fibres stretched about 30% at 25°C; his results are shown in *Figure 83*. The stress decreases almost

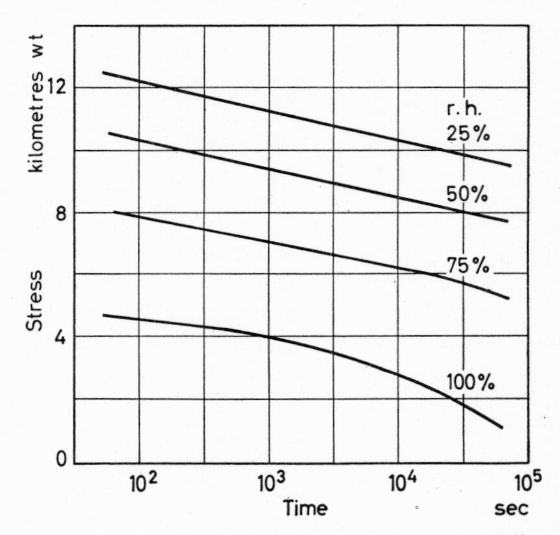

Figure 83. Effect of relative humidity on relaxation of wool fibres stretched about 30% at 25°C (after Speakman (9))

linearly with increase in log(time) by about the same absolute amount at humidities from 25 to 75% r.h., and rather faster at 100% r.h. The relative amount of relaxation is considerably greater at the higher relative humidities. Thus, in 1,000 minutes at 25% r.h., the stress relaxes by 23% of its value at a time one minute after application of the extension, at 75% r.h. the percentage relaxation is 33% and at 100% r.h. the percentage relaxation is 73%.

Burleigh and Wakeham (*10*) studied the relaxation of cotton and viscose rayon tyre cords at various humidities after loading in two seconds to a stress somewhat less than the yield stress. Again the relaxation increased with increasing humidity up to 70% r.h., but at 100% r.h. the rate of relaxation was less than that in the dry cords, after an initial rapid fall in stress which was completed within one minute. These authors calculated activation energies from the hyperbolic tangent relation between stress and time, based on Eyring's theory of rate processes, namely,

$$\log_e \tanh \tfrac{1}{2}\alpha p = -\alpha E_1 Kt + \log_e \tanh \tfrac{1}{2}\alpha p_0 \qquad \ldots.(2)$$

where p is the stress at time t, p_0 is the initial stress at time $t = 0$, α is a parameter, E_1 is the contribution to the elastic modulus from the structural elements which flow and K is the frequency with which the flowing segments jump backwards and forwards due to thermal agitation. From K the energy of activation is calculated. Unfortunately, the values calculated by Burleigh and Wakeham are too high because they assumed that all the stress would eventually relax, i.e., they took the value of E_1 as that due to both primary and secondary bonds.

Some data for the relaxation behaviour of cotton and viscose rayon fibres at relative humidities from 0 to 100% r.h., and in water, have been given by Andersen (*11*). The times required for that part of the stress which relaxes to fall to half its initial value are recorded in Table 15. The time required increases with the extension imposed on the fibre, but the values given in Table 15 have been averaged

TABLE 15

TIME IN SECONDS FOR PART OF STRESS WHICH RELAXES TO FALL TO HALF ITS INITIAL VALUE AT 20°C

Fibre \ Relative humidity (%)	0	37	70	100	wet
Cotton	—	3·44	3·81	2·20	0·60
Viscose rayon	15·4	11·2	7·08	1·99	0·57
Viscose staple fibre	9·24	3·78	2·45	2·69	0·33

over all the stresses at any one humidity because the effect of humidity is the point of interest here. It is seen that, as the relative humidity increases, the time to reach half the initial stress decreases considerably, i.e., the relative rate of relaxation increases, and the increase is of similar magnitude for each fibre. The rate of decay of stress in the wet fibres is about four times as great as that for fibres conditioned at 100% r.h. This may be due to incomplete conditioning at 100% r.h. A similar fast initial decay of stress at 100% r.h.

was observed by Burleigh and Wakeham (*10*) for cotton and rayon cords, but it is clear from their experiments that relaxation has not ceased after a few minutes as assumed by Andersen, but that it continues at a relatively slow rate for much longer times.

The observations of Burleigh and Wakeham are confirmed by results for viscose rayon given by Wegener and Luyken (*12*). These authors extended viscose rayon yarn at a constant rate (0·66%/s) and observed the relaxation of tension for 5 minutes when the yarn was held at extensions from 2% to 16% at relative humidities of 45, 65, 85 and 100%. Under these conditions the decay of tension, p, with time, t, can be represented by the equation

$$p = C(t+a)^{-n}$$

where C, a and n are constants.

The percentage of the initial stress which decayed in 5 minutes (see Table 16) was rather less at 45% r.h. than at 65% or 85% r.h.

TABLE 16

PERCENTAGE OF INITIAL STRESS WHICH DECAYS IN 5 MINUTES

Extension (%) \ Relative humidity (%)	45	65	85	100
2	47	48	54	33
6	40	46	43	28
10	34	41	38	31
14	31	38	36	33

At 100% r.h. only about 30% of the initial stress decayed in 5 minutes, i.e., even less than the decay at 45% r.h., in agreement with Burleigh and Wakeham.

TORSIONAL PROPERTIES

Although the tensile properties of textiles are of first importance, the torsional properties are also important in relation to processes such as the spinning and doubling of staple-fibre yarns and in the production of crêpe yarns. For example, in spinning, the twist is transmitted from one element of yarn to another and its distribution depends on the resistance to, and recovery from, twist in successive portions of the yarn. The periodic high twist in a mule-spun yarn is due partly to the decay of twist as it runs from the spindle to the rollers.

Stress–Strain Relations

Torque–twist curves for most fibres are similar to their corresponding load–extension curves (*13*). Thus, for example, with viscose rayon, as twist is inserted the torque first increases in proportion to the twist and then a yield point is reached, after which the torque continues to increase with twist, but at a much slower rate. As twisting is continued the rate of increase of torque begins to increase again until finally the fibre ruptures. Humidity has a large effect on the initial resistance to twist and also on the yield point, as is shown in *Figure 84*.

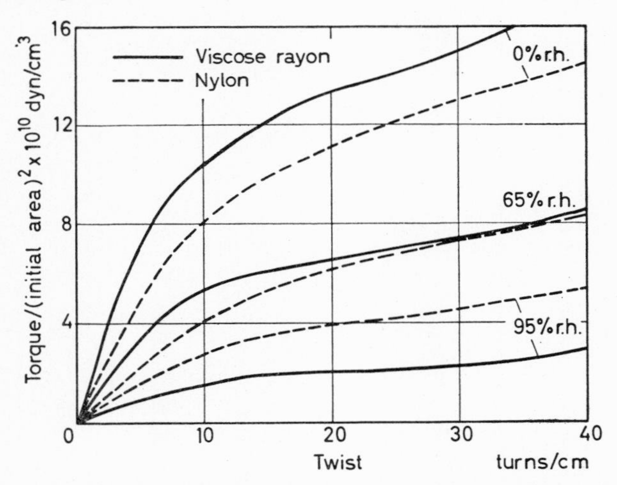

Figure 84. Effect of relative humidity on torque–twist curves for rayon and nylon filaments at 20°C (after Morton and Permanyer (13))

If the torque required to produce a twist of one turn per cm is defined as the rigidity of the fibre, Γ, then the modulus of rigidity, G, is given by

$$G = \Gamma/\epsilon A^2 \qquad \ldots.(3)$$

where A is the area of cross-section and ϵ is a shape factor which is equal to unity for a fibre of circular cross-section and does not vary much from unity unless the fibre section deviates greatly from circular. For example, cotton fibres which have highly irregular cross-sections have an average shape factor of 0·74. Some values of rigidity modulus are given in Table 17, together with approximate ratios of the rigidity modulus of the bone-dry fibre to that of the wet fibre. The rigidity of wool fibres is highly sensitive to moisture and even nylon filaments, which absorb comparatively little water, have a bone-dry rigidity which is three times the wet rigidity.

TABLE 17

MODULI OF RIGIDITY AT 65% R.H. AND RATIOS OF RIGIDITY FOR BONE-DRY AND WET FIBRES

Fibre	Rigidity modulus (10^{10} dyn/cm^2)	Ratio of bone-dry to wet rigidity
Viscose rayon	1·1	30
Wool	1·1	16
Silk	2·2	12
Cotton	2·5	9
Cellulose acetate	0·8	3
Nylon	0·5	3

The shape of the curve relating rigidity modulus to moisture regain is of some interest. Thus, for cotton, Peirce (*14*) found that, when the logarithm of the torsional rigidity, Γ, is plotted against regain, r, the points lie on a straight line: the torsional rigidity is halved by the addition of 10% of moisture. Thus, it was found that

$$\log_e(\Gamma/\Gamma_0) = -0{\cdot}07r \qquad \ldots.(4)$$

Similar relations (*15*) have been found for ramie, mercerized cotton and viscose rayon, and they can be expressed in the single equation (5) which applies, from 0 to 90% r.h., to all cellulose fibres so far examined; thus,

$$\log_e(G/G_{65}) = -0{\cdot}82\,[(r/r_{65})-1)] \qquad \ldots.(5)$$

where the modulus of rigidity, G, corresponds to a moisture regain, r, and r_{65} is the moisture regain at 65% r.h. in absorption. This equation shows that the relation between rigidity and regain is known as soon as the modulus of rigidity and moisture regain at 65% r.h. have been measured.

The way in which the rigidity modulus of wool fibres depends on regain differs from that for cellulose fibres, as shown in *Figure 85*. For the first few per cent of moisture absorbed, the fall in modulus is quite small. From 5 to 25% regain the decrease in rigidity modulus is large and above 25% regain there is little further change. Nylon gives a curve intermediate in shape between that for cellulose fibres and wool.

The fall in rigidity observed with all these fibres is consistent with the supposition that this is caused by the breaking of hydrogen bonds between chain molecules in the non-crystalline regions and that, at saturation regain, one molecule of water is bound to each accessible polar group which would otherwise be linked by means of a hydrogen bond to a similar polar group in a neighbouring chain molecule.

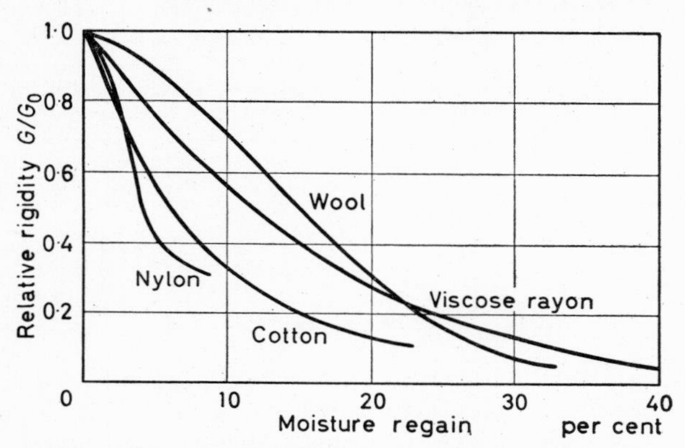

Figure 85. Relation between rigidity modulus and moisture regain

Speakman (*16*) has analysed the curve for wool and found that the fall in rigidity is complete when approximately one molecule of bound water is associated with each amino-acid residue, i.e., with each peptide group. The water that combines with the hydrophilic side-chains has no appreciable effect on the rigidity modulus.

Shear strength

If sufficient twist is inserted in a fibre, rupture will occur by virtue of the shear stress developed. Finlayson (*17*) has measured the shear stress at rupture for several types of fibre by means of a simple device consisting of three plates with a $\frac{3}{32}$-in. diameter hole drilled through the three together and into which is packed a parallelized bundle of fibres. The two outer plates are rigidly fastened to each other and the centre plate is withdrawn to shear the fibres. In this method the shear strength is measured at a pre-determined place along the length of the fibre, so that, for comparison of these shear strengths with tensile strength, it seems reasonable to restrict the test length in the tensile test to, say, 0·2 mm. The values of tensile and shear strength so measured are given in Table 18, both at 65% r.h. and wet. In the last two columns are recorded the ratios of wet strength to air-dry strength, both in shear and in tension. It has already been remarked that the tensile strength of wet native cellulose fibres, such as cotton and flax, is equal to, or greater than, the air-dry strength. In shear, the wet strength appears to be less than the air-dry strength for all types of fibre. The range of variation in shear strength, amongst the different fibres tested, is much less than

TABLE 18

SHEAR AND TENSILE STRENGTH OF TEXTILE FIBRES

Fibre	Shear strength (nominal) (10^8 dyn/cm^2)		Tensile strength (nominal) (10^8 dyn/cm^2)		$\frac{\text{Wet strength} \times 100}{\text{Air-dry strength}}$	
	65%	wet	65%	wet	Shear	Tension
Flax	12·1	10·0	180	197	83	110
Cotton	12·9	10·5	120	120	82	100
Viscose rayon	9·6	4·2	46	23	44	50
Cuprammonium rayon	9·6	6·2	37	22	65	60
Cellulose acetate	7·6	6·3	24	17	83	70
Fortisan H	15·7	12·7	143	120	81	84
Silk	15·5	11·4	74	59	74	80
Nylon	12·8	10·9	66	61	85	92

the corresponding variation in tensile strength. Similarly, the range of variation covered by the ratio of wet strength to air-dry strength is much less in shear than in tension.

Relaxation

When dealing with the tensile properties it was shown that, if a fibre is stretched and held at constant length, the stress will relax appreciably. Similarly, if a fibre is twisted and the twist held constant, the torque will decay.

Morton and Permanyer (*18*) measured the torsional relaxation of viscose rayon filaments at 0–90% r.h. and found that, by plotting the logarithm of the torque against the logarithm of the time, straight lines could be fitted to the observations made between 5 seconds and 24 hours after twisting ceased. At low twists (5 turns/cm), the relative rate of decay of torque was much higher at 90% r.h. than at 0% r.h.: at higher twists (20 and 40 turns/cm), humidity had little effect on the fraction of initial torque that decayed in a given time. For cellulose acetate and nylon, the fraction of torque that decayed in a given time was little affected by humidity at any of the above values of twist.

REFERENCES

1 B. Farrow, *J. Text. Inst.*, **42,** T534 (1951).
2 L. Rose and J. D. Griffiths, *J. Text. Inst.*, **39,** P265 (1948).
3 Z. A. Rogovin and R. S. Neiman, *J. Appl. Chem.* (*U.S.S.R.*), **18,** 208 (1945).
4 R. L. Steinberger, *Text. Res. J.*, **6,** 191, 267 (1936).
5 H. Leaderman, *Elastic and Creep Properties of Filamentous Materials, etc.* The Textile Foundation, Washington, D.C., 1943.
6 H. D. Holland, G. Halsey and H. Eyring, *Text. Res. J.*, **16,** 201 (1946).
7 C. H. Reichardt, G. Halsey and H. Eyring, *Text. Res. J.*, **16,** 382 (1946).
8 J. J. Press, *J. Appl. Phys.*, **14,** 224 (1943).
9 J. B. Speakman, *Proc. Roy. Soc.*, **B103,** 377 (1928).
10 E. G. Burleigh, Jr., and H. Wakeham, *Text. Res. J.*, **17,** 245 (1947).
11 F. Andersen, *Trans. Danish Acad. Tech. Sci.*, No. 3 (1950).
12 W. Wegener and E. Luyken, *Melliand Textilber.*, **33,** 37 (1952).
13 W. E. Morton and F. Permanyer, *J. Text. Inst.*, **40,** T371 (1949).
14 F. H. Clayton and F. T. Peirce, *J. Text. Inst.*, **20,** T315 (1929); F. T. Peirce, *J. Text. Inst.*, **20,** T133 (1929).
15 R. Meredith, *J. Text. Inst.*, **48,** T163 (1957).
16 J. B. Speakman, *Trans. Faraday Soc.*, **40,** 6 (1944).
17 D. Finlayson, *J. Text. Inst.*, **38,** T50 (1947).
18 W. E. Morton and F. Permanyer, Lectures at Leeds University, March 19th and 20th, 1948.
19 D. D. Gagliardi and I. J. Gruntfast, *Text. Res. J.*, **20,** 180 (1950).

CHAPTER 13

FIBRES AND LIQUID WATER

By J. W. S. Hearle

CAPILLARY WATER

So far attention has been devoted to studies of absorption of moisture from humid atmospheres. Many stages of textile processing and paper manufacture use liquid water, and the retention of this by fibres is of considerable importance. The moisture content, as previously discussed, may be about half the dry weight, whereas in paper pulps the moisture will be up to 10 times the dry weight. The greater part of this will be retained by capillary forces.

The retention of liquid water has been discussed by Barkas and Hallan (*1*), who consider the rise in level when a capillary tube is dipped into water. The water will be drawn up against gravity and hence will be under a hydrostatic tension. The water surface forms a curved meniscus and the hydrostatic pressure, P, is related to the radius of curvature, r, by

$$P = \frac{2\gamma}{r}\cos\theta \qquad \ldots.(1)$$

where γ is the surface tension and θ the contact angle. In addition, thermodynamics show that, at the air–water interface in the capillary, the water exerts a lower vapour pressure and the hydrostatic pressure in the water can be calculated approximately by

$$P = -\frac{RT}{Mu}\log_e \frac{h}{h_0} \qquad \ldots.(2)$$

where R is the gas constant, T is the absolute temperature, M is the molecular weight of water, u is the specific volume of water, and h/h_0 is the relative humidity (i.e., vapour pressure h of water at tension P/saturated vapour pressure h_0).

Barkas goes on to consider a horizontal capillary filled with water and not in contact with any outside source of liquid water. In a saturated atmosphere the liquid surfaces at the end of the capillary will be planar. Reduction of the relative humidity will cause a slight evaporation, thereby creating a curved meniscus described by equation (1) and creating a tension in the liquid in equilibrium with the surrounding relative humidity according to equation (2). Further reduction of the relative humidity will cause evaporation of water until the curvature of the meniscus is equal to the radius of the capillary. The meniscus is then hemispherical and the slightest further reduction will cause the liquid to evaporate and the meniscus to retract into the tube. Hence, at any given relative humidity, all the capillaries with a radius less than a given value will be filled with water and all those greater than this will be empty.

TABLE 19

RELATIVE HUMIDITY OVER CAPILLARY WATER AT 22°C
(ZERO CONTACT ANGLE)

Tension (P) cm of mercury	Relative humidity (h/h_0)	Capillary radius (r) cm
0	1	∞
1	0·99999	$1{\cdot}09 \times 10^{-2}$
5	0·99995	$2{\cdot}16 \times 10^{-3}$
10	0·99990	$1{\cdot}09 \times 10^{-3}$
14	0·99986	$7{\cdot}75 \times 10^{-4}$
20	0·99980	$5{\cdot}43 \times 10^{-4}$
100	0·99901	$1{\cdot}09 \times 10^{-4}$
1,000	0·99025	$1{\cdot}09 \times 10^{-5}$
10,000	0·90668	$1{\cdot}09 \times 10^{-6}$
50,000	0·61270	$2{\cdot}18 \times 10^{-7}$

Table 19 gives some values of corresponding relative humidities, tensions and radii of curvature calculated from equations (1) and (2). It must be noted, however, that the term 'curvature of a meniscus' ceases to be meaningful when the dimensions of the capillaries in which the meniscus lies are of the same order of size as molecular dimensions (*ca.* 10^{-7} cm), that is, when the relative humidity lies below 60–70%. Below this limit all the water must be held by molecular forces.

Circular capillaries do not necessarily exist in practice. Whatever the shape of the curved meniscus, at any point on its surface two principal radii of curvature, r_1 and r_2, may be ascribed. The liquid tension is given by substituting $1/r_1 + 1/r_2$ for $2/r$ in equation (1). The values of r given in Table 19 must therefore be considered to refer to uniform radii of curvature equivalent to the more complex forms of menisci encountered in practice.

Furthermore, porous materials will seldom possess capillaries of uniform cross-section. For any relative humidity, the capillary will be filled to a point where a meniscus of suitable size can exist in which the double curvature corresponds to the liquid tension. A tapering capillary, for example, will gradually empty as the relative humidity is decreased and gradually fill as the relative humidity is increased.

Any crack, pore or space capable of holding liquid water under tension may be treated as a capillary and any meniscus can be characterized in terms of a circular meniscus of equivalent curvature. These ideas may now be applied to the drying of water-logged fibres.

DRYING OF A MAT OF FIBRES IN A WATER-LOGGED STATE

In a mat of water-logged fibres, from which water has been removed by drainage under gravity and not by drying or pressing, the bulk of the water will be held in the capillary network between the fibres. When exposed to an atmosphere with a humidity slightly below saturation, the mat will dry out until the equilibrium conditions described by equations (1) and (2) are reached. The hydrostatic tension acting throughout causes consolidation and compression of the mat. Should the inter-fibre spaces be too large to hold water at the existing tension, the water menisci will recede to a new point of equilibrium. Thus, on decreasing the relative humidity, the water will enter the inter-fibre capillary network. The more easily the fibre mat is compressed, the smaller will be the inter-fibre capillaries at any given tension, and hence the higher the tension which can be applied before air penetrates. Capillary water will never be completely removed, but will still be held round the points of contact between fibres, in small fibre cavities and, particularly in paper, in the small cracks between the fibrils formed during the beating process.

In Barkas's work, attention is devoted to conditions corresponding to humidities very close to saturation where the water is held predominantly in capillaries. The moisture retained in the void spaces in a fibre mat under static equilibrium was measured by Strachan (*2*). He subjected the fibre mat to a certain external compressing force and thereby squeezed out a great portion of the inter-fibre capillary water. The remainder he called 'water of imbibition'. A centrifuge method has been used to some extent in recent years (*3–6*). In this technique the fibre mat is subjected to an increased gravitational field. As a result, the liquid tension will be zero at the bottom of the mat and increase to a maximum at the top. Furthermore, the increased gravitational field will cause an increased compression on the fibres in the mat; this compression will be greatest at the bottom and zero at the top of the mat. These effects will result in the moisture content being different for different layers of the mat. In the method used by Barkas and Hallan for the study of paper pulps, the mat is put on a porous plate and a certain tension is applied. This technique also measures the equilibrium moisture retention in pulps and can be used for a whole series of increasing or decreasing tensions. Under these conditions, apart from the liquid tension within its voids, the fibre mat itself is subjected only to the normal gravitational field.

POROUS PLATE TECHNIQUE

The porous plate technique has been applied by Schofield (*7*) and Haines (*8*) in the study of moisture retention in soils. It has later been used by Preston and Nimkar (*9*) in the study of textile materials.

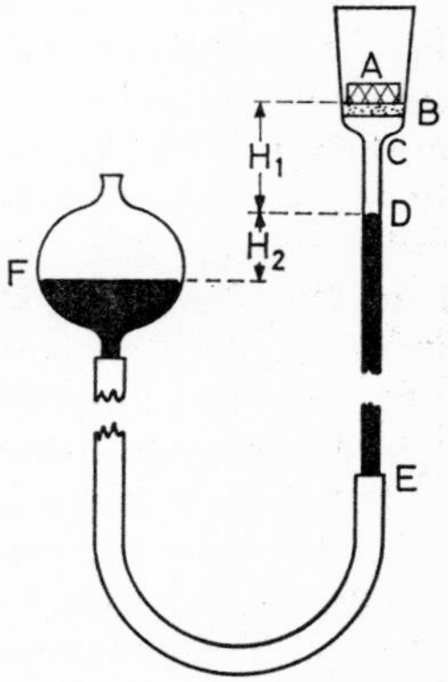

Figure 86. Apparatus for study of moisture retention by textiles
(By courtesy of *Proc. Tech. Sect.*, British Paper & Board Makers' Assoc., 1953)

The simplest form of apparatus, shown in *Figure 86*, will suffice to explain the principles of the method. The fibre mat A is resting on the porous plate B of a glass crucible, which is connected to a glass tube CE and a rubber tube connecting this with a glass container F. The space between B and D is filled with water and DEF contains mercury. The liquid tension at the bottom of the fibre mat is calculated from the heights H_1 and H_2 and the densities of water and mercury. Because of the high density of mercury, the height required to obtain the desired tensions is not excessive and it has been found convenient to express the tension as a mercury head. At the top of the fibre mat, the tension will be slightly higher than at the bottom, because of the water head through the thickness of the mat itself. Except for very small tensions, the change of tension through the thickness of the mat is negligible compared with the total barometric tension applied, and in these investigations a uniform tension throughout the mat may be assumed. The tube CE is calibrated and the change of position of the interface at D gives a measure of the volume of water passing through the plate.

As described earlier, the water under a given tension exerts a certain reduced vapour pressure and all stable water surfaces attain the same equivalent curvature. This is valid both for the fibre mat and for that part of the porous plate which is exposed to the air, so that the largest tension that can be applied to the water in the mat will be limited by the size of the biggest capillaries in the porous plate.

After the reservoir F has been adjusted to give zero tension in the liquid at the surface of the plate, the water-logged fibre mat A is placed on the plate B. By lowering F, a tension is applied to the water in the mat and some of it will be sucked into the space BD. When the position of D has remained constant over a period of 30 min, equilibrium is assumed to have been reached. This may take altogether between one and two hours. Increased equilibrium tensions can be applied until, when the desired maximum tension has been reached, the experiment is either stopped or the tension is gradually reduced and readings taken during absorption. Finally, the mat is removed from the plate, weighed and dried to constant weight at 105°C, thus giving its moisture content at the tension pertaining when it was removed. It is thus possible to calculate the moisture contents at all tensions and the results are plotted as a tension–moisture content isotherm (later termed a tension isotherm), as shown in *Figure 88.*

In practical use, some minor additions and alterations to the simple apparatus of *Figure 86* have been found advantageous. The most important of these is to arrange for the tube CE to be horizontal over the length along which the water–mercury boundary moves, so that the applied tension will remain sensibly constant during the time required to establish equilibrium; in the original set-up shown in *Figure 86* the tension is gradually changing. For the horizontal tube, a capillary of about 2-mm diameter and 50-cm length is used.

Loss of water from the fibre mat by evaporation must be avoided. A device (*Figure 87*) is therefore fitted on top of the crucible so that the only path from the mat to the atmosphere is through a small chamber L, which contains cotton wool saturated with water, and then through a long glass capillary M. In this way, loss of water by evaporation is practically eliminated without affecting the atmospheric pressure on the sample.

If the water is left under tension for any length of time, air bubbles will sometimes appear under the plate. This effect may be largely overcome by using air-free water, obtained by boiling and cooling under vacuum.

The curve given in *Figure 88* is typical of the results obtained by this method. The moisture content of the fibre mat, expressed as the weight of water per unit weight of dry fibre, is given on the horizontal axis. The initial water/fibre ratio has in most cases been about 10.

Figure 87. Modification to apparatus for study of moisture retention by textiles
(By courtesy of B.P. & B.M.A., 1953)

In this region, the slope of the curve is very small, because even a small change in tension at this stage is sufficient to cause compression, resulting in considerable water removal. The slope increases

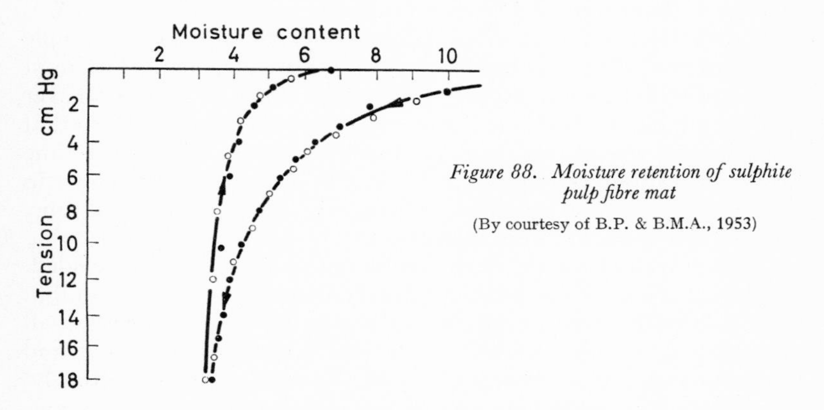

Figure 88. Moisture retention of sulphite pulp fibre mat
(By courtesy of B.P. & B.M.A., 1953)

gradually as the tension is increased, but, for high tensions (say, above 11 or 12 cm of mercury), the line is again very nearly straight. This has been verified up to a tension of 22 cm of mercury. In most cases, however, a maximum tension of 18 cm of mercury has been used.

The absorption curve does not coincide with the desorption one, but shows lower moisture contents at all tensions, and the path it follows will depend on the moisture content from which absorption started. Even at zero, the mat is far from reaching the moisture content from which the desorption started. An 'open' hysteresis loop is therefore formed, showing that the compression of the mat during desorption is partly irreversible, due to plastic deformation.

In *Figure 88*, the values for two different fibre mats made from the same source (a sulphite pulp) have been plotted (dots and circles, respectively). This shows that a satisfactory degree of reproducibility is obtained for these experiments with the method finally adopted.

EXPERIMENTS ON TEXTILE FIBRES

Preston and Nimkar (*9*), in their experiments on textile fibres, found that a more rapid approach to equilibrium could be achieved

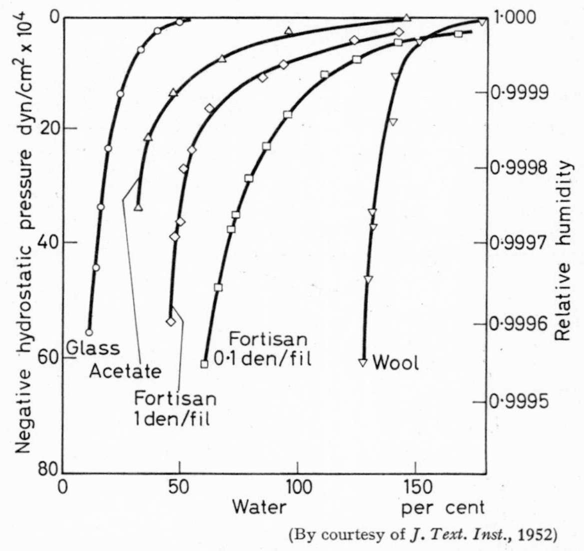

(By courtesy of *J. Text. Inst.*, 1952)

Figure 89. Relation between moisture retention by fibres and hydrostatic tension

by winding yarn on a porous cylinder connected to a controlled vacuum.

Figure 89 gives examples of their results for the water retained by various fibres plotted against the hydrostatic tension. Values of the equivalent humidity obtained from equation (2) are also shown. The results of experiments of this sort are an extension of the absorp-

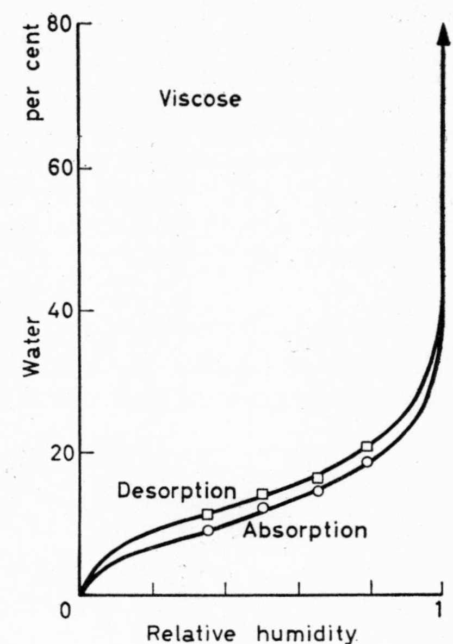

Figure 90. Absorption–desorption curves for viscose rayon at lower humidities
(By courtesy of *J. Text. Inst.*, 1952)

tion data at lower humidities as shown in *Figure 90*. A set of comparative results for different fibres under a constant hydrostatic tension is given in Table 20.

TABLE 20

Fibres	Water retention (%)	
	−30 cm Hg	1,000 *g*, 5 minutes
Viscose yarn, flat twist	106	103
Cuprammonium yarn, flat twist	100	89
Viscose steamed yarn, flat twist	90	86
Viscose fabric	86	86
Fortisan 0·1-den yarn, flat twist	70	63
Silk yarn, flat twist	55	52
Cotton yarn	52	48
Fortisan 1-den yarn, flat twist	48	48
Cellulose acetate yarn, flat twist	31	31
Nylon yarn, flat twist	14	16
Glass yarn, flat twist	15	13
Wool, loose	133	45

BEHAVIOUR ON CENTRIFUGATION

Preston, Nimkar and Gundavda (*10*) have investigated the alternative method of removing water by centrifugation. They have derived a theoretical relation for the amount of water retained, by means of the following reasoning.

'The water in the capillary spaces between fibres can be considered on the usual theory of capillary rise. The simplifying assumption is made that the water surface at the lower end of a capillary has a negligible curvature. The water in any capillary will be held in an equilibrium between surface and centrifugal forces after a steady state has been reached.

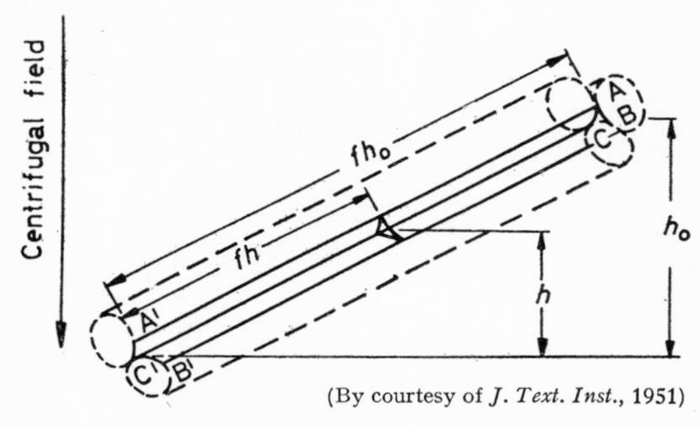

(By courtesy of *J. Text. Inst.*, 1951)

Figure 91. Capillary channels formed by groups of contiguous fibres

'Groups of contiguous fibres will form capillary channels of a form such as that represented by ABC, A'B'C' in *Figure 91*. The equilibrium equation can be written down. The pull of the surface forces is the product of the surface tension, γ, the cosine of the contact angle, $\cos \theta$, and the length of the periphery of the cross-section of the capillary, l. The centrifugal pull is the product of the cross-sectional area, a, the height of the capillary filled with liquid, h, the density of the liquid, σ, and the centrifugal field, g. Then, for equilibrium in a capillary parallel to the centrifugal field:

$$\gamma \cos \theta . l = ah\sigma g \qquad \ldots . (3)$$

On the assumption that the capillary is uniform the volume filled with water is ah. From equation (3),

$$ah = \frac{\gamma \cos \theta . l}{\sigma g} \qquad \ldots . (4)$$

'If the capillary is not parallel to the centrifugal field, as in *Figure 91*, then its length will be greater than its height in the direction of the field. Let the ratio of length to height be f. Then the volume of water in the capillary is given by:

$$fah = \frac{f\gamma \cos \theta . l}{\sigma g} \qquad \ldots . (5)$$

The mass of water in the capillary is given by:

$$\sigma fah = \frac{f\gamma \cos \theta . l}{g} \qquad \ldots . (6)$$

Now, the assembly of fibres forming the capillary has a mass related to its total length, fh_0, where h_0 is the total height parallel to the centrifugal field. In the case of a uniform structure of fibres forming the capillary there will be a certain mass of fibres associated with unit length. Let the mass constant be c; then, the mass, m, of the fibres forming the capillary is given by:

$$m = cfh_0 \qquad \ldots . (7)$$

'The mass of water retained per unit mass of fibres, R, from equations (6) and (7) is:

$$R = \frac{f\gamma \cos \theta . l}{cfh_0 g} = \frac{\gamma \cos \theta . l}{gh_0 c} \qquad \ldots . (8)$$

In this equation the quotient l/c is the length of periphery where surface forces act per unit mass of fibres. With a series of uniform fibres of similar shape and packing, the term l/c can be expressed in more convenient terms as follows. Because of the assumed similar geometric arrangement, the periphery of the capillary, l, is directly proportional to the periphery of a fibre and this in turn is proportional to $\sqrt{A}$, where A is the cross-sectional area of a fibre. But, the cross-sectional area of a fibre is proportional to its denier, d, divided by its density, ρ. Hence, $l \propto \sqrt{d/\rho}$, and, by a similar argument $c \propto d$.

Therefore,

$$l/c \propto \frac{\sqrt{d}}{d\sqrt{\rho}} \propto \frac{1}{\sqrt{\rho d}} \qquad \ldots . (9)$$

Hence, equation (8) can be rewritten

$$R = \frac{\gamma}{g} . \cos \theta . \frac{1}{h_0} . \frac{1}{\sqrt{\rho d}} . \text{(constant)} \qquad \ldots . (10)$$

'From equation (10) it follows that the relative mass of water retained should increase linearly with surface tension, the reciprocal of the centrifugal field, the cosine of the contact angle, the reciprocal of the total height of the capillaries in the direction of the field and the reciprocal of the root of the product of density and denier of the fibres.'

Their experimental results confirm this equation, although they find that anything which resulted in a tighter packing of the fibres reduced the amount of water retained. Some results for various fibres are included in Table 20.

ACKNOWLEDGEMENT

The first part of this chapter is based on a paper by the author's former colleague, the late Dr. W. W. Barkas (*1*).

REFERENCES

1 W. W. Barkas and R. Hallan, *Proc. Tech. Sect. B.P. & B.M.A.*, **34,** 289 (1953).
2 J. Strachan, *Proc. Tech. Sect. B.P. & B.M.A.*, **34,** 139 (1953).
3 G. Jayme and L. Rothamel, *Das Papier*, **2,** 7 (1948).
4 R. Renaud, *Bull. ATIP*, **1,** 14 (1947).
5 R. Renaud, *Bull. ATIP*, **2,** 98 (1948).
6 G. van Nederveen, *Papierwereld*, **6,** 291 (1952).
7 R. K. Schofield, *Third Inter. Cong. Soil Sci.*, **2,** 38 (1935).
8 W. B. Haines, *J. Agric. Sci.*, **20,** 97 (1930).
9 J. M. Preston and M. V. Nimkar, *J. Text. Inst.*, **43,** T402 (1952).
10 J. M. Preston, M.V. Nimkar and S. P. Gundavda, *J. Text. Inst.*, **42,** T79 (1951).

NAME INDEX

SUBJECT INDEX

SUBJECT INDEX

SUBJECT INDEX